Oceanography

M. Grant Gross
University of Washington
Smithsonian Institution

CHARLES E. MERRILL BOOKS, INC., COLUMBUS, OHIO

Merrill Physical Science Series

Robert J. Foster and Walter A. Gong, *Editors*

San Jose State College

1 2 3 4 5 6 7 8 9 10 11 12 13 — 75 74 73 72 71 70 69 68 67

Library of Congress Catalog Card Number: 67-25451

PRINTED IN THE UNITED STATES OF AMERICA

Editors' Foreword

As curricula become more crowded in this age of rapidly expanding knowledge and specialization, more and more colleges and universities are turning to integrated interdisciplinary courses to transmit the basic essentials of science to non-science majors. We believe that the rigid structure of most physical science textbooks has imposed severe limitations on instruction in these courses. Far too often, instructors trained in various specialities have had to attempt to fit the wide range of goals, abilities, and backgrounds of their students to a textbook, when the converse, of course, would be much more satisfactory.

In January, 1965, the editors, five authors, and representatives of Charles E. Merrill Books, Inc., met in San Francisco to implement a new conception of physical science textbooks. The result is the *Physical Science Series,* a collection of specially written, integrated materials in short, paperback form for the college physical science program. Our coordinated efforts were directed by three vital principles.

1. The Series permits maximum flexibility of use by instructors and students. Each paperback textbook represents a five-to-seven-week section of instruction, and may be used in any sequence or combination desired by the instructor. In addition, freedom of sequence within a single book is possible. This flexibility is especially helpful in courses that include laboratory experience. In this way it is hoped that each instructor will be free to choose the most appropriate materials for his students.

2. The subject areas are portrayed in a valid manner. Each book is written by a specialist in a different discipline—physicist, chemist, astronomer, meteorologist, geologist, and science educator. Thus, in place of a homogeneous blend of textbook statements, the individual paperback textbooks have distinctive scientific flavors. The student can discover both the contrasts and underlying unities in the viewpoints of scientists in different disciplines; he can, for example, compare the approach of the physicist, who performs lab-

oratory experiments, with that of the geologist, who depends largely on observations of natural occurrences.

3. Scientific communication is clear, concise, and correct. Each author is both academician and experienced teacher. He has designed instruction around carefully selected scientific principles logically related to laws, definitions, and associated phenomena. Technology is used to provide illustrative examples rather than a myriad of facts to be remembered. Mathematical reasoning is used only when the sciences are made more (not less) understandable for the non-science major. Scientific jargon and excessive nomenclature are avoided.

San Jose, California   *Robert J. Foster*

November, 1965   *Walter A. Gong*

Table of Contents

Chapter 4
WATER AND ITS PROPERTIES   **40**

Chapter 5
SEA WATER — A SALT SOLUTION   **51**

Chapter 6
THE OPEN OCEAN   **65**

Chapter 7
OCEAN CURRENTS 81

Chapter 8
WAVES AND TIDES 98

Chapter 1

Earth – The Water Planet

Earth is the water planet. The abundant water-laden clouds, and the rain falling on an Oregon forest, attest to the copious amounts of water on the earth's surface. Since the crust first solidified, water has been extracted from the earth's interior to collect in depressions. Nearly 71 per cent of the earth's surface (see Frontispiece) is now overlain by a blanket of water, averaging 3,730 m (meters) deep. At any instant only a small fraction of the earth's water is present in the atmosphere, or retained by the land in lakes, or locked in glaciers and ice caps. Nearly all the water remains in the oceans.

Most of the earth's population lives within a few hundred kilometers of the ocean shore. For these people the oceans have long served as a recreational area, food source, and as a highway for commerce. Even to those living far from the ocean, its influence on daily life is great. Not only do the oceans supply the water necessary for life, but they also store and then release much of the solar energy that powers earth's atmospheric circulation, causing our weather. Simply by contrasting the large daily temperature changes in the desert with the even temperatures of coastal climates, we can see the role that the oceans play as a climatic buffer.

Life on the earth is thought to have originated in a primordial ocean. Since then the ocean has served and still serves as home for most living things. In our slightly salty blood, we carry a reminder that our remote ancestors gave up marine life to populate the continents. Many land-dwelling animals still have not broken their dependence on a body of water for reproduction and early development of their young. We still look to the sea to supply food, and in some areas much of the protein in the diet comes from marine organisms.

In short, ours is a water-conditioned existence, and by studying the oceans we can learn about a dominant feature of our environment. With better understanding we may someday be able to predict changes in the oceanic and atmospheric circulation that affect our lives. Equally important is the necessity to learn enough about the oceans to permit us to use them more fully for such functions as waste disposal, without destroying them as a source of food or as recreational areas.

DISTRIBUTION OF LAND AND WATER

Geophysicists studying the physics of the earth, or geochemists investigating the earth's chemistry, consider the earth to consist of concentric shells (Fig. 1-1), each shell having a distinctive chemical and physical

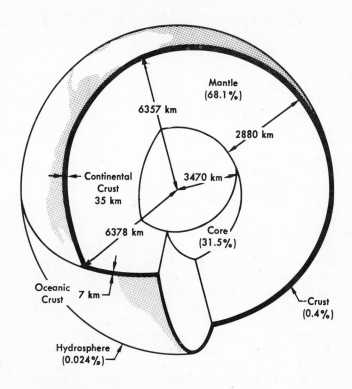

Fig. 1-1. Internal structure of the earth showing the concentric shells, their relative mass (in per cent) and thickness. (Modified after E. C. Robertson, "The Interior of the Earth. An Elementary Description," Geological Survey Circular 532 [Washington, D. C.: Government Printing Office, 1966] 10 p.)

composition. When viewed from this perspective, the earth's metallic **core** and the rocks of the **mantle** constitute 99.6 per cent of its mass. The rocks of the continents and ocean basins, the oceans, and the atmosphere, amount to only 0.4 per cent, of which the ocean and atmosphere are only a very small fraction. Thus in terms of the earth as a whole, the oceans constitute an insignificant fraction of its mass — a thin film of water on a nearly smooth sphere.

Restricting our view to the earth's surface (510 million square kilometers), we find the oceans covering 361 million square kilometers or 70.8

per cent. Although the average depth of the ocean is 3,730 m, it is insignificant (1/1700) compared to the earth's dimensions (Fig. 1-1). This thin film of water accounts for 86.5 per cent of the water not combined in rock. Excluding the water retained in the pores of sedimentary rocks, the oceans contain 97 per cent of the earth's water (Table 1-1).

Table 1-1.   Mass and Distribution of the Hydrosphere*

	Mass $(10^{15}$ tons$)$†	Relative abundance $(\%)$
Sea water	1410	86.5
Lakes, rivers	0.5	0.03
Continental ice	22	1.3
Water vapor in atmosphere	0.013	.001
Water in sediments and sedimentary rocks	200	12.2
Total	1632	100

*After A. Poldervaart, "Chemistry of the earth's crust," *Geological Society of America Special Paper* 62 (1955), p. 121.
†See Appendix for discussion of exponential notation.

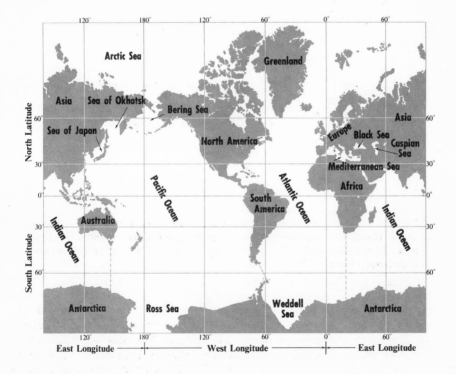

Fig. 1-2.   Distribution of continents and oceans on the earth's surface.

The oceans and continents are unevenly distributed over the earth's surface. Each of the great continental blocks has an oceanic area opposite to it on the other side of the earth. We say that the oceans and continents tend to be **antipodal.** We should also note that the continents tend to have a triangular shape, well illustrated by Africa and the Americas (Fig. 1-2). Many scientists suspect that these relationships are not accidental but are the consequence of some unknown forces or processes active at some time in the earth's history — perhaps still at work.

Most of the land on the earth (67 per cent) lies in the Northern Hemisphere (Fig. 1-3). Between **latitudes*** 45° and 70°N there is more land

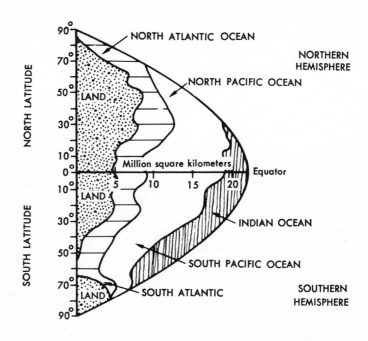

Fig. 1-3. Distribution of land and ocean. (Data from G. Wüst, W. Brogmus, and E. Noodt, "Die zonale Verteilung von Salzgehalt, Niederschlag, Verdunstung, Temperatur und Dichte an der Oberfläche der Ozeane," Kieler Meeresforschungen Band X [1954], 139.)

than water, although the sea covers 61 per cent of the Northern Hemisphere. *If we consider the Northern Hemisphere to be the land hemisphere, the Southern is clearly the water hemisphere.* Not only does the ocean cover 81 per cent of the earth's surface between latitudes 40° and 65°S, but there is almost no land to impede the atmospheric or oceanic circula-

---

*The parallels of latitude connect points equidistant north or south of the equator.

tion. Here in the "Roaring Forties" of the Southern Hemisphere we have an almost completely ocean-dominated earth.

Since the oceans in the Southern Hemisphere are not completely separated by land masses, the organisms which live by floating in the surface waters can migrate rather freely, that is if they can tolerate changes in the salt content and temperature of the water. Migrations of land-dwelling plants and animals and marine organisms in the Northern Hemisphere oceans are restricted by the natural barriers which surround them. Viewed from space looking down on Antarctica (see Frontispiece), the world ocean would appear to be a broad band surrounding Antarctica with three northward projecting gulfs.

In fact we are dealing with only one ocean, but for convenience we divide it into three parts: the Atlantic (including the Arctic Sea), Indian, and Pacific Oceans. Lacking useful natural boundaries, we must draw arbitrary lines along meridians of **longitude*** to separate them. We separate the Pacific Ocean from the Indian Ocean by a line running southward from Australia to Antarctica along 150°E, approximately through the island of Tasmania. The island areas north of Australia form a convenient and more or less natural boundary between the Pacific and Indian Oceans. On the north, the Bering Strait is a partial barrier to ocean currents as it separates the Pacific Ocean and Arctic Sea. A line between Cape Horn (the southern tip of South America) and Antarctica, approximately at latitude 60°W, divides the Pacific and Atlantic Oceans.

The **Pacific Ocean** is the largest of the three ocean basins (Fig. 1-3). In fact, it is nearly as large as the Indian and Atlantic Oceans combined and contains slightly more than half of the water in the world ocean. The Pacific has the greatest average depth (3,940 m) because it includes few shallow marginal seas. It also contains the deepest areas in the oceans, nearly 11,000 m in several **trenches** along its western margin. Trenches with associated island areas are one of the most distinctive features of the Pacific Ocean. These areas of active volcanoes and frequent earthquakes form the Pacific "Rim of Fire," apparently areas of active mountain building.

We should also note that relatively few rivers discharge into the Pacific Ocean. Its surface area is ten times greater than the land drained by all the streams flowing into it (Table 1-2). Thus, we should expect that the Pacific is less affected by the presence of the continents than are the other oceans. Conditions in the Pacific Ocean, especially in the Southern Hemisphere, most closely resemble what we should expect on a completely water-covered earth. Such effect as the continents have on the Pacific Ocean is most noticable in its northern regions.

In distinct contrast to the Pacific, the **Atlantic Ocean** is a relatively narrow, twisted body of water, bounded by more or less parallel continental margins. Including the Arctic Sea, the Atlantic Ocean has the greatest north-south extent, and it connects the northern and southern polar regions

---

*North-south lines connecting points equidistant (east or west) from the Prime Meridian (0° longitude) through Greenwich, England.

Table 1-2. Areas and Depths of the Oceans*

Oceans†	Ocean Area (10⁶km²)	Land area drained‡ (10⁶km²)	Ocean area / Drainage area	Average depth (m)
Pacific	180	18	10	3940
Atlantic	107	67	1.6	3310
Indian	74	17	4.3	3840
World ocean	361	102	3.6	3730

*In part after H. W. Menard and S. M. Smith "Hypsometry of ocean basin provinces," *Journal of Geophysical Research,* 71 (1966), 4305.

†Includes adjacent seas. Arctic, Mediterranean, and Black Seas included in the Atlantic Ocean.

‡Excludes Antarctica and continental areas with no exterior drainage. After J. Lyman, "Chemical considerations," in *Conference on Physical and Chemical Properties of Sea Water,* Publication 600 (Washington, D.C.: National Academy of Sciences-National Research Council, 1959), p. 89.

(Fig. 1-3). Because of the many shallow adjacent seas (Caribbean, Mediterranean, Baltic, Gulf of Mexico) and the Arctic Sea, the Atlantic is the shallowest of the three oceans — average depth 3,310 m. Many rivers, including the world's two largest, the Amazon and Congo rivers, discharge into the Atlantic. The abundance of rivers can be appreciated from the fact that its surface area is only 1.6 times the area drained by the rivers flowing into the Atlantic. As we shall see later, this abundance of river discharge is noticeable in the lowered salt content of the surface waters in the Arctic Sea.

Unlike the Pacific, the Atlantic Ocean has few islands. The two island-arc systems, the West Indies in the North Atlantic and the South Sandwich Islands of the South Atlantic, may actually be part of the Pacific's crustal structure. Other islands (Iceland, the Azores, St. Paul's Rocks, Tristan da Cunha) are associated with the Mid-Atlantic Ridge, which we discuss in the next chapter.

The **Indian Ocean** is bordered by Africa and Asia. We separate the Indian and Atlantic Oceans by a north-south line between Cape Good Hope, the southern tip of Africa, and Antarctica along longitude 20°E. The Indian Ocean extends only a short distance across the equator into the Northern Hemisphere; its northern limit lies at roughly 25°N. It has few islands or adjacent seas. The average depth of the Indian Ocean (3,840 m) is intermediate between the Atlantic and Pacific Ocean averages. The surface area is 4.3 times the size of the area drained by streams discharging into it. The very large Ganges and Brahmaputra rivers flow into its northern edge.

Because of the proximity of the large continental masses of Africa and Asia, conditions on the northern Indian Ocean vary radically during the year. The winds change direction with the seasons. During the northeast monsoons of winter (in the Northern Hemisphere) the ocean surface currents are distinctly different from those during the southwest monsoons of summer. This will be discussed more fully in a later chapter.

MARGINAL SEAS

Parts of the coastal regions of each ocean are separated by land barriers to form **seas**. Not only do these seas have rather well defined boundaries, but most have distinctive oceanographic properties as well. The unique water properties of each sea are a consequence of (1) restricted communication of the sea water with the open ocean, (2) the influence of the adjacent continent, such as variable wind patterns, and (3) an excess of precipitation and river discharge. We discuss conditions in the coastal oceans more fully in Chapter 9.

Largest of the marginal seas, the **Arctic Sea** forms the nearly isolated northern extension of the Atlantic Ocean (see Frontispiece). Including this northern part, which extends across the pole down to the Bering Strait at 66°N, the Atlantic Ocean extends to about 70°S, almost halfway around the earth in a north-south direction. The waters of the Arctic Sea are diluted by the discharge of many rivers, including two large Siberian rivers, the Lena and Yenisei. These and other rivers keep the Arctic surface waters substantially less salty than the adjacent North Atlantic Ocean. Sea ice covers approximately 70 per cent of the Arctic Sea throughout the year. During the Northern winter, the remainder of the Arctic Sea is covered with sea ice as the surface water freezes.

Next in size are the **Caribbean Sea-Gulf of Mexico** between North and South America and the **Mediterranean Sea** between Europe and Africa. Both lie near 30°N, in the warm subtropical climatic belt that includes the earth's great deserts, such as the Sahara and Gobi. Both seas are characterized by an excess of evaporation. Even the Mississippi River flowing into the northern Gulf of Mexico does not contribute enough fresh, water to compensate for the excess of evaporation. Consequently, the surface waters of both seas are characterized by high salt content relative to the rest of the ocean.

The **Black Sea** is connected to the world ocean by the Bosphorus, a narrow channel with a mean width of 700 m and a minimum depth of approximately 40 m. Obviously such a restricted channel does not permit free communication with the Mediterranean Sea. At times in the past, this tenuous connection with the world ocean has been completely severed. The **Caspian Sea** to the east of the Black Sea was also once connected to the ocean. Subsequent land movements and changes in sea level have eliminated its connection.

AGE AND ORIGIN OF SEA WATER

Oceans are an ancient feature of the earth's surface. Through time the records of their origins have been obscured and are now the subject of much scientific discussion. Most scientists believe that the oceans and the continents originated as a consequence of the same processes. They disagree most about the timing of these events and the rate at which the oceans and continents formed.

Many geologists believe that the oceans formed through the gradual release of water at the earth's surface through volcanic action, causing the removal of water originally bound in the rocks of the earth's interior. These scientists estimate that the amount of water released through the earth's history can account for our present oceans.

Some of the most ancient rocks (approximately 3 billion years old) yet dated by radioactive means are sedimentary rocks containing pebbles and other features which suggest that the sediments were formed in water. Since the earth is thought to have formed about 5 billion years ago, these data suggest that large bodies of water have been present on the earth's surface through more than half of its history.

Life appeared in the oceans at an early date. Some of these ancient rocks (2.7 billion years old) appear to have been formed by algae, primitive one-celled plants which still exist in the ocean. By careful observation and use of the electron microscope, scientists have shown that other rocks, approximately 2 billion years old, contain the remains of bacteria-like organisms.

We know little about the ocean's beginnings, and even less about possible changes in sea water composition since that time. Reasoning from the apparent similarities between living organisms and the abundant fossils in rocks as old as 600 million years, geologists have concluded that the composition of sea water has changed little in this period. Probably oxygen has become more abundant in the atmosphere due to photosynthesis by plants, which release oxygen as they manufacture food from carbon dioxide, water and sunlight. We have almost no clues about the composition of sea water during the time preceding the appearance of marine organisms with preservable skeletons or other hard parts.

The abundance of many elements found in sea water can be accounted for by assuming that they represent the material removed in solution from the weathering of silicate rocks on land. Geochemists, who study the chemistry of the earth and its oceans, have concluded that the salt now contained in one liter of sea water could have been extracted by weathering 600 grams of rock and dissolving the more easily soluble parts in sea water.

Unfortunately such calculations do not account for the abundance in sea water of such major chemical constituents as chlorine, sulfur, or boron. The source of these elements is still not satisfactorily explained, although it has been suggested that they may have been released, along with water, by volcanoes.

PERMANENCE OF SHORELINES AND OCEAN BASINS

Although oceans are an ancient feature of the earth's surface, the **shorelines**—boundaries between land and water—have probably changed location many times. The location of shorelines can change as continents rise and fall, or as the sea surface rises or falls relative to a stable continent. Ample evidence indicates that all of these processes have caused changes in shorelines.

Large changes in the relative location of the continental blocks may have occurred during earth's history, perhaps several times. This still controversial idea is supported by the parallelism of the present shorelines on both sides of the Atlantic Ocean (Fig. 1-2). The west coast of Africa and the east coast of South America are examples of the closeness of this fit. Many scientists think that these continents were once joined, before the formation of the Atlantic Ocean about 200 million years ago resulted in their present separation. Other supporting evidence for drifting of the continents includes the former distribution of now extinct plants and animals, former locations of the earth's magnetic poles, and the record of ancient ice ages on continents, especially in the Southern Hemisphere.

Not all scientists support the concept of continental drift. They contend that other mechanisms can account for part or all of the distributions involved. We will not consider the problem further, except to point out that if continental drift has occurred in the past, it may still be occurring. This would have profound effects on the oceans; not only would surface currents be affected by changes in the positions of the continents, but the circulation of the deeper waters would be influenced as well.

Slow vertical movements of the continental blocks are occurring at present. Doubtlessly this has also occurred repeatedly during earth's history. Elevated former shorelines along the California coast and now submerged Greek and Roman temples around the Mediterranean Sea provide convincing evidence of such movements and the resulting changes in location of the shorelines.

Less obvious are the probable vertical movements of the ocean floor. Such changes in the ocean floor affect sea level by changing the volume of the ocean basin. Substantial vertical movements of a large part of the ocean floor would cause a rise in sea level to compensate for the diminished volume of the ocean basin. Similarly, subsidence of the ocean floor would be accompanied by a fall in sea level.

Many geologists believe that such vertical movements of the sea floor are not uncommon. Charles Darwin pointed out in 1842 that the abundance of **atolls** — ring-shaped bands of reefs and low sand islands surrounding a lagoon — in the central west Pacific Ocean could be explained by a widespread subsidence of the sea floor. Such movements of the sea floor probably could cause a rise or fall of the sea surface of a few hundred meters. The cause of such vertical movements of the sea floor or continents is still a hotly debated question. One explanation is that they result from chemical and physical changes in the underlying mantle rocks.

There is ample evidence in the sedimentary rocks deposited on the now emerged continents that the continental blocks have frequently been partially covered by large shallow seas. Probably the expanse of these former continental seas resulted from various combinations of vertical movements of the sea floor and the continental blocks.

Changes in the amount of water in the ocean would also cause changes in sea level. If the idea of a gradual accumulation of water in the oceans is correct, then sea level must have risen gradually during the earth's development. The record of the ancient sea levels is too poorly preserved to provide an unequivocal answer to this point.

Large and relatively sudden changes in sea level accompany the development and disappearance of large ice sheets on the earth's surface. The water stored on land in such continent-sized **glaciers** comes from the ocean. As a result, sea level is lowered as the glaciers form and is elevated as the glaciers melt.

The earth at present seems to be emerging from an ice age. During the maximum development of the glaciers more than 10,000 years ago, the sea stood 100 to 200 m below its present level. Much of the shallowly submerged continental margin was then dry land. Asia and North America were connected by a land bridge, now covered by the shallow Bering and Chukchi seas. Early man migrated across this bridge from Asia to populate North and South America. Mammoths grazed on the now submerged Atlantic continental margin of North America. Rivers cut extensive valley systems on these now submerged offshore lands and the present sea floor around many island groups such as Indonesia.

When the ice melted about 10,000 years ago, sea level rose, flooding many of the former river valleys. On glacier-carved mountainous coasts, the picturesque steep-sided fiords were formed. It is estimated that if all the water remaining in the Antarctic and Greenland ice sheets were returned to the ocean, sea level would rise about 50 m. Large portions of the low lying coastal plains would be flooded. Many of our present coastal cities would become hazards to navigation and a hunting ground for future generations of diving anthropologists, much as certain ancient Greek and Roman cities are now.

In short, present distribution of land and ocean is probably only a quick look at a continually changing picture. Because of the structure of the continents and deep ocean basins (discussed in the next chapter), it seems probable, however, that the relative proportions of land and water have remained relatively constant.

GENERALIZATIONS AND ASSUMPTIONS ABOUT THE OCEANS

The oceans are interconnected, so that processes acting on sea water, even in a remote basin, eventually affect the entire ocean. For example, the warm arid climate of the land around the Mediterranean Sea causes its surface waters to evaporate at a greater rate than do most Atlantic waters, and hence to be somewhat saltier. Warm, salty water from the Mediterranean enters the Atlantic Ocean along the bottom of the Strait of Gibralter and can be detected below the surface over a large part of the Atlantic.

As a consequence of its long history, *we assume that the world ocean is presently changing very slowly, if at all, with time.* This important assumption, the **steady state assumption,** means that oceanographers can use data taken as much as a hundred years ago, to study ocean processes. The importance of this is evident when one considers the enormous area of the oceans and the difficulty of getting nearly simultaneous data.

Another consequence of the ocean's great age and slow rate of change is that *sea water is generally well mixed.* If we assume that the water in the deep ocean returns to the surface in 1,000 to 2,000 years, and that the oceans have probably existed for 3 billion years, we can estimate that the ocean waters have been mixed more than a million times. As one noted chemist has pointed out, few solutions in the chemistry laboratory are so thoroughly stirred. Thus, we should not be surprised to find that sea salts are nearly identical, regardless of where the sea water samples are collected. The apparently uniform chemical composition of the ocean may arise from its long history and from our restricted vantage point, covering about 100 years for a feature that has existed 20 million times as long.

STUDY OF THE OCEANS

Oceanography derives its name from the study of ocean geography — the mapping of ocean boundaries and the delineation of ocean currents. The oceans have proven to be a formidable object to study, and they remain the least known part of the earth's surface.

Study of the oceans began with the exploration of the earth's surface. Because of the importance of shipping and ocean travel, the mapping of the ocean margins was an important part of the early explorations. Of the exploring expeditions which began in the fifteenth century, two were especially important for the mapping of the oceans. The Spanish-financed Portuguese nobleman Ferdinando Magellan (1480?-1521) explored the Pacific Ocean and circumnavigated the earth by water. The English navigator Captain James Cook (1728-1779) established the outlines for much of the Pacific Ocean and showed that an ice-covered continent (Antarctica) was located at the South Pole.

During this period there were important advances in instrumentation for navigation. Devices for accurately measuring angles at sea (today we use the sextant for this purpose) permitted navigators to determine their latitude. The magnetic compass, known in western Europe since the twelfth century, indicated direction even when the sun or stars were hidden from view. With the development in 1761 of a practical chronometer (an accurate ship's clock) navigators were finally able to determine their longitude. By comparing the time of local noon (when the sun is highest in the sky) with the time in Greenwich, England, Cook was able to determine his longitude well enough to make reasonably accurate maps of the Pacific Ocean.

Benjamin Franklin (1706-1790) published a chart (1770) showing the location of the Gulf Stream, of great importance to sailing vessels. Scientific studies of the oceans did not begin until the nineteenth century. Edward Forbes (1815-1854), an early biological oceanographer, studied life in the ocean and postulated that no life existed below about 600 meters. Although proven to be erroneous, this idea stimulated many other scientists to work on problems of marine biology.

Charles Darwin (1809-1882) was the naturalist on the exploring voyage of the "Beagle" (1831-1836). His observations on coral reefs led to a brilliant hypothesis about their formation, which we will discuss in a later chapter. Even if Darwin had not formulated his famous theory on the origin of the species through evolution, he would have become famous through his work on coral reefs.

The American scientist Matthew Fontaine Maury (1806-1873) is credited with being the father of oceanography. Beginning in the early 1840's, Maury synthesized the data available from many years of observations made aboard sailing vessels. From these he compiled charts showing the winds and currents for each month of the year. Maury also wrote the first textbook on oceanography — *The Physical Geography of the Sea.* Both the charts and the book had a wide impact at the time and demonstrated the economic advantages to shipping that could be gained from systematic investigations of the oceans.

The first extensive and systematic investigation of the world ocean was undertaken between 1872 and 1876 by the British-financed *"Challenger" Deep-Sea Expedition* (Fig. 1-4) under the direction of Sir C. Wyville Thomson (1830-1882). From this expedition came a fifty-volume report

H.M.S. "Challenger."

Fig. 1-4. The H. M. S. "Challenger," the ship used on the Challenger Expedition.

which has greatly influenced the development of oceanography and is still a valuable source of information for oceanographers. Part of the credit for the success of the Challenger Expedition goes to Sir John Murray (1841-1914) who directed the Challenger Expedition Office after Thomson's death, and who wrote or helped write five of the fifty volumes.

Among the remarkable men who have contributed to our knowledge of the oceans, the Norwegian Fridtjof Nansen (1861-1930) deserves special mention. This zoologist, artist, and Nobel Peace Prize winner, was the first man to cross the Greenland ice cap. He also tested his theory of surface currents in the Arctic Sea by causing a specially reinforced ship, "Fram," to be frozen into the Arctic pack ice, so that it would drift across the Arctic Sea. When it became obvious that his ship would not reach the North Pole, Nansen and a companion set out on foot over the ice toward the pole. Although he failed to reach his goal (by 375 km), Nansen went further north than anyone had gone before. A water sampling bottle (Fig. 5-6) designed by Nansen is still one of the standard oceanographic sampling devices.

QUESTIONS

1. What are the advantages of dividing the world ocean as is done in Fig. 1-2? What are the disadvantages?
2. What evidence has been used to support the idea of continental drift? If the continents have drifted apart, which ocean has probably been most affected? Which one least affected?
3. What are some of the economic gains to be realized from a detailed and accurate forecast of ocean currents, their position and strength?
4. List the important geographic feature(s) of each ocean. How does each feature affect the ocean?
5. Determine which part of the ocean is antipodal (directly opposite on the earth's surface) to each continent. (This is most easily done using a globe.)
6. Determine the latitude and longitude of your building. What is its antipodal point?
7. Which ocean has conditions most nearly resembling those on a water-covered earth? Explain the reasons for your choice.
8. List and briefly discuss some of the processes which may cause changes in the positions of shorelines.
9. What evidence might be used to demonstrate that the Caspian Sea was once connected to the world ocean?
10. Which are the "Seven Seas" referred to in literature? In which ocean would each be included using the boundaries given in Fig. 1-2?

SUPPLEMENTARY READING

Bailey, H. S., Jr., "The Voyage of the Challenger," *Scientific American,* May, 1953.

Bates, D. R., *The Earth and Its Atmosphere.* New York: Basic Books, Inc., 1957. General reference, elementary.

Beiser, Arthur, and the Editors of Life, *The Earth.* New York: Time, Incorporated, 1963.

Carson, Rachel, *The Sea Around Us.* Rev. ed. New York: Oxford University Press, 1961. Nontechnical.

Deacon, G. E. R., ed., *Seas, Maps, and Men: An Atlas-History of Man's Exploration of the Oceans.* Garden City, N. Y.: Doubleday and Company, Inc., 1962. General reference, nicely illustrated.

Dietrich, Günter, *General Oceanography: An Introduction.* Translated by Feodor Ostapoff. New York: Interscience Publishers, 1963. General reference. Technical, good bibliography.

Engel, Leonard, and the Editors of Life, *The Sea.* New York: Time, Incorporated, 1963.

Hurley, Patrick M., *How Old is the Earth?* Garden City, N. Y.: Anchor Books, Doubleday and Company, Inc., 1959.

Sverdrup, H. U., Martin W. Johnson, and Richard H. Fleming, *The Oceans: Their Physics, Chemistry, and General Biology.* Englewood Cliffs, N. J.: Prentice-Hall, Inc., 1942. General reference, technical.

Von Arx, William S., *An Introduction to Physical Oceanography.* Reading, Mass.: Addison-Wesley Publishing Company, Inc., 1962. Technical, good bibliography.

William, Jerome, *Oceanography: An Introduction to the Marine Sciences.* Boston, Mass.: Little, Brown, and Company, Inc., 1962. General reference, intermediate in difficulty.

Chapter 2

The Ocean Floor

We begin our study of the oceans with the ocean floors. Their exploration began with crude lead-weighted ropes or wires lowered from sailing vessels. Few depth determinations were obtained in this way, because of the difficulty and expense of making each measurement. With few data points available, scientists thought for many years that the ocean bottom was a flat, nearly featureless plain.

This changed drastically after the echo sounder (Fig. 2-1), developed

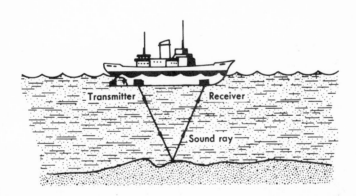

Fig. 2-1. Echo sounder on an oceanographic survey ship. Water depth = ½ speed of sound x echo time. (After Robert J. Foster, *Geology.* [Columbus, Ohio: Charles E. Merrill Books, Inc., 1966], p. 106.)

in World War I, was used to explore the ocean floor. By accurately determining the elapsed time between the emission of a strong sound pulse, and the arrival back at the ship of its echo from the bottom, the depth of the underlying ocean floor can be quickly and accurately determined. This method was first employed for making numerous individual and isolated measurements of ocean depths.

After World War II, equipment became widely available for making continuous "soundings" and recording a **profile** (or vertical cross-section) of the ocean floor over which the ship passed. By combining thousands of such sounding lines, oceanographers have prepared maps of bottom topography. From these maps, scientists have found earth-circling mountain ranges, enormous east-west trending cliffs, and deep, narrow trenches near the ocean margins, especially in the Pacific Ocean. In short, *the ocean bottom is not a featureless plain, but a surface as complicated and irregular as the more familiar land surfaces.*

ELEVATIONS AND DEPRESSIONS

To begin our examination of the various sea-floor features, let us look at the relative frequency of land elevations and ocean depths. From maps of the land surface and sea floor, one can determine the percentage of the earth's surface that lies at a particular depth or elevation. When plotted on a graph, these data form a **hypsometric curve** (Fig. 2-2). It is important to remember that this is not a profile of the ocean bottom.

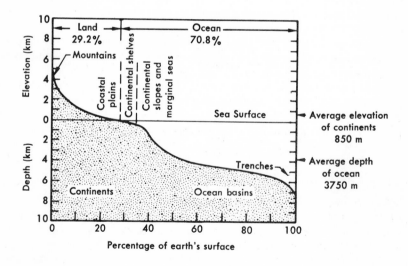

Fig. 2-2. Hypsometric curve showing the percentage of the earth's surface above any given depth or elevation. (After H. U. Sverdrup, M. W. Johnson, and R. H. Fleming, *The Oceans: Their Physics, Chemistry, and General Biology.* [Englewood Cliffs, N. J.: Prentice-Hall, Inc., 1942] p. 19.)

A hypsometric curve reveals the scarcity of mountains higher than 6,000 m or parts of the ocean floor deeper than 6,000 m. These extreme heights or depths constitute less than 1 per cent of the earth's surface. We also find that the average depth of the oceans is 3,730 m and that the average land elevation is approximately 850 m. The average level of the earth's crust is 2,430 m below sea level. In other words, *if we planed off the continents and filled the ocean basins with the debris, the earth would be covered uniformly by water 2,430 m deep.*

The hypsometric curve also reveals that elevations and depths on the earth's crust have two dominant levels (the nearly horizontal parts of the curve in Fig. 2-2). One, averaging around 300 m above sea level, is the low-lying continental surface. The other, between 4,000 and 5,000 m below sea level, is deep-ocean bottom. These levels are the result of fundamental differences in composition and structure between ocean basins and continents. It seems probable that these two levels have been nearly constant relative to each other through much of the earth's history.

The antipodal distribution of the continents and oceans has not yet been explained, but geophysicists have shown that the continents and ocean basins have distinctly different structures. Thick blocks of granitic rocks, of a **density** — mass per unit volume — about 2.8 g/cm^3 (Fig. 1-1), form the **continental blocks.** The **ocean basins** are formed of much thinner layers of basaltic rock, of average density about 3.0 g/cm^3. Both structures essentially float in the underlying mantle, with an apparent average density of about 4.5 g/cm^3. The continents float higher than the ocean basins because granitic rocks are less dense than basaltic rocks.

Most of the information about crustal structure is obtained by indirect means. Studies of the passage of seismic waves from distant earthquakes, local variations in the force of gravity, heat flow from the earth's interior, and earth magnetism have been especially informative. Using such geophysical data, scientists have found that the ocean floor at depths less than 2,000 m generally exhibits continental-type structures. The ocean floor deeper than 4,000 m almost invariably has a thin basaltic crust, quite unlike the continents.

TOPOGRAPHY OF THE SEA FLOOR

Let us explore the ocean bottom topography by taking an imaginary trip across an ocean. Using a continuously operating echo sounder, we could obtain a profile similar to Fig. 2-3. Obviously the bottom features seen and their size and exact location would be determined by the route chosen.

First we cross the **continental shelf,** on the average about 65 km wide, bordering the continent. This shallow area, usually less than 130 m deep, slopes gently seaward. Its bottom topography resembles the adjacent land. If the coastal area has rugged topography, so does the continental shelf, for example, off Southern California. Where the coastal area has low hills or plains, the adjacent continental shelf is likely to have subdued topo-

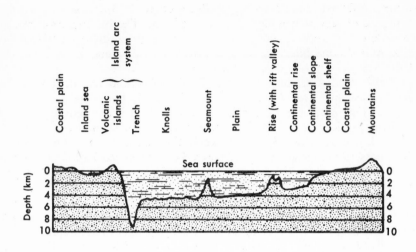

Fig. 2-3. Schematic profile of an ocean floor showing typical features of the deep-ocean floor and adjacent areas. (Vertical scale greatly exaggerated.)

graphy, nearly flat plains or low hills, as it does off the Mid-Atlantic coast of the United States.

As our ship continues seaward, the ocean deepens rapidly as we cross the **continental slope.** The boundary between the continental shelf and slope is the point at which the bottom slopes become much steeper. This is the **continental shelf break,** usually occurring at depths around 130 m. Off Antarctica, however, the shelf break occurs at depths around 500 m.

The base of the continental slope at approximately 2,000 m marks the approximate edge of the continents (Fig. 2-4). Both the continental shelf and slope — referred to as the **continental margin** — are structurally part of the continents even though covered by sea water. *The exposed and submerged parts of the continents account for about 40 per cent of the earth's surface* (Fig. 2-2).

Not only do the continental slopes mark the edges of the continents, but they form the largest continuous slopes on the earth's surface. None of the imposing mountain fronts of the western United States compare with the continental slope in height or length. If the oceans were dry and we could observe the earth's surface from space, the Pacific continental slopes would be especially imposing. Backed by some of the highest mountains on earth, the total drop from the peaks of the South American Andes to the Peru-Chile trench is approximately 13,000 m, nearly half again as high as Mount Everest (8,850 m) in the Himalaya Mountains of Asia.

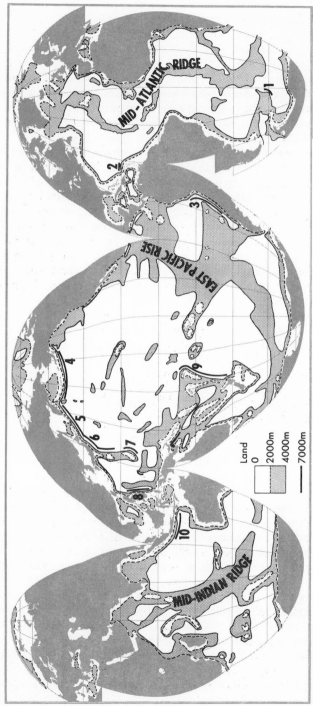

Land
0
2000m
4000m
7000m

Fig. 2-4. Topography of the ocean floor. (After U. S. Naval Oceanographic Office, "Chart of the World," 10th edition, H.O. 1262A.)

In many areas, the continental slopes are cut by impressively large, V-shaped submarine canyons. Up to 1,200 m deep, some of these canyons rival Arizona's Grand Canyon of the Colorado River in size and depth. Many of these canyons are associated with the mouths of major rivers; some examples are the Congo or Hudson canyons, or Astoria Canyon near the mouth of the Columbia River. Others are less obviously related to present river mouths. Submarine canyons are thought to have been cut or at least strongly affected by **turbidity currents,** dense, sediment-laden currents flowing along the sea floor.

If our ship's course happened to follow a canyon beyond the seaward edge of the continental slope, the echo sounder would show a large, featureless apron sloping very gently seaward. These aprons, built of sediment from the continent, are thought to be formed when turbidity currents pass from the narrow submarine canyon and deposit sediment on the unrestricted open sea floor. If our echo sounder were sensitive enough, it would likely show rather shallow seachannels on the apron surface. It appears that turbidity currents flow through these channels. In many respects, these aprons resemble the deposits built by intermittent streams on land as they emerge from mountains and deposit their sediment on a valley floor in the desert.

These aprons, built at the mouths of many canyons, coalesce to form a thick sediment deposit, the **continental rise.** In most cases the sediment cover is thick enough to bury preexisting bottom irregularities, forming a nearly featureless bottom. Although present in the North Pacific Ocean, such features are more common in the Atlantic and Northern Indian Oceans, which receive the discharge of many large rivers.

As the submerged continental margins are left behind, we find ourselves in waters 4,000 to 6,000 m deep — the **ocean basin** proper (Fig. 2-4). *The deep-ocean basin accounts for nearly 30 per cent of the earth's surface.*

Soon after traversing the continental rise, the echo sounder shows that we are crossing a more irregular sea floor, broadly arched with numerous submarine volcanoes. Between the volcanoes are flat-bottomed basins, presumably sediment-floored. We find some steep-sided valleys, bounded by **faults** — fractures in the crust along which one side has been displaced relative to the other. This rough terrain is part of a mid-ocean rise.

Mid-ocean **rises** and **ridges,** nearly 23 per cent of the earth's surface (Table 2-1), occur in all the major oceans. Some lie near the center of the ocean basin (Fig. 2-4), for example, the **Mid-Atlantic Ridge** and the **Mid-Indian Ridge.** But in the South Pacific, the **East Pacific Rise** lies near the South American continent. Many experts believe that it intersects North America in the Gulf of California, and goes out into the Pacific Ocean again near the California-Oregon boundary.

Having crossed this mid-ocean rise, we again find a nearly flat, featureless sea bottom, or **plain,** sometimes called an abyssal plain. It, like the continental rise, is built primarily of sediment derived from the continent and buries any preexisting rough topography. It is important to note that the plain, as shown in Fig. 2-3, is nearly 1,000 m deeper than the con-

Table 2-1. Physiographic Provinces of the Ocean Bottom.*

Ocean†	Shelf and Slope (%)	Conti- nental Rise (%)	Ocean Basin (%)	Volcanoes and Volcanic Ridges, etc. (%)	Rise and Ridge (%)	Trenches (%)
Pacific	13.1	2.7	43.0	2.5	35.9	2.9
Atlantic	19.4	8.5	38.0	2.1	31.2	0.7
Indian	9.1	5.7	49.2	5.4	30.2	0.3
World ocean	15.3	5.3	41.8	3.1	32.7	1.7
Earth's surface	10.8	3.7	29.5	2.2	23.1	1.2

*After H. W. Menard and S. M. Smith, "Hypsometry of ocean basin provinces," *Journal of Geophysical Research,* 71 (1966), 4305.
†Includes adjacent seas; for example, Arctic Sea included in Atlantic Ocean.

tinental rise on the landward side of the oceanic rise. As we will see later, this can be caused by the damming effect of the mountainous topography which inhibits or prevents the seaward movement of bottom-transported sediment. Much of the sediment transported onto the sea floor is thus trapped and cannot be carried out into the deeper plains.

Proceeding further from the North American continent, the echo sounder records the presence of many low hills or **knòlls,** rising less than 1,000 m above the sea floor. It appears that the sediment cover in these areas is not thick enough to bury completely the irregularities on the sea floor. Investigations of these deeply submerged hills reveals that many have no sediment cover. Instead, basaltic rocks are often recovered from them during dredging operations.

Volcanoes appear on the echo sounder records, individually or in groups. It is estimated that nearly 10,000 of these volcanoes occur on the sea floor. Only the tops of the largest ones project above the ocean surface as islands. The Hawaiian Islands are an example of such large island-forming volcanoes. Rising nearly 9,000 m from the adjacent sea floor, the volcanoes forming the Hawaiian chain are larger than the largest mountain ranges on the continents.

Near the western edge of the Pacific Ocean we cross the spectacular **trenches,** which seem to mark the transition between the continents and the ocean basins, especially in the Pacific. These long, narrow, steep-sided depressions contain the greatest depths in the oceans; several of the western Pacific trenches are nearly 11,000 m deep (Table 2-2). Broad areas of low relief roughly parallel the seaward side of the trenches.

Table 2-2. Maximum Depths of Deep-Sea Trenches*

	Depths (meters)
ATLANTIC OCEAN	
South Sandwich Trench (1)†	8,400
Puerto Rico Trench (2)	9,200
PACIFIC OCEAN	
Peru-Chile Trench (3)	8,050
Aleutian Trench (4)	8,100
Kuril-Kamchatka Trench (5)	10,500
Japan Trench (6)	9,800
Marianas Trench (7)	11,000
Philippine Trench (8)	10,000
Kermadec-Tonga Trench (9)	10,800
INDIAN OCEAN	
Java Trench (10)	7,460

*Data from U. S. Naval Oceanographic Office, Washington, D. C., and from R. L. Fisher and H. H. Hess, "Trenches" in *The Sea: Ideas and Observations on Progress in the Study of the Seas,* vol. 3, ed. M. N. Hill (New York: Interscience Publishers, 1963), pp. 418-419.
†Trench locations are indicated by numbers on Fig. 2-4.

Curved groups of islands with numerous volcanoes often border the landward side. Together with the associated trenches they are known as **island-arc systems.** These systems on the continent-ocean boundaries are apparently areas of active mountain building; some of the highest mountains on land border the island-arc systems. The frequent earthquakes and numerous active volcanoes appear to be manifestations of large-scale movements of the earth's crust in such regions. Island arcs are most common along the Pacific margin, forming the so-called "Pacific Rim of Fire."

Shallow marginal seas occur between the continents and some of the largest island-arc systems, such as the Japanese and Philippine Islands (Fig. 1-2). These seas are apparently floored by thick sediment deposits. The sediment particles brought into the ocean by rivers are trapped near the continent. The trenches also appear to be potentially good sediment traps, which are filled in only a few places. The abundance of sediment traps bordering the North Pacific probably accounts in large part for the great depth of the North Pacific ocean floor. Much of it lies below 6,000 m because it has not been filled by thick sediment deposits.

Another striking feature of the ocean floor is a system of east-west trending **fracture zones.** Consisting of a series of steep cliffs, rough topography, and belts of **seamounts,** the fracture zones extend for several thousand kilometers across the Pacific Ocean. At least four major ones apparently intersect the North American continent. In each, the fracture zones seem to have some fundamental relationship to continental topography or structure. For example, the **Mendocino fracture zone** (at approximately 40°N) intersects the northern California coast approximately at

Cape Mendocino where the spectacular **San Andreas fault** goes onto the continental shelf.

CORAL REEFS AND ATOLLS

Among the most picturesque structures in the oceans are **coral reefs.** These wave-resistant structures are built by carbonate-secreting organisms, mainly **corals** and **encrusting algae.** Corals — small colonial animals — are the most conspicuous part of most living reefs. The much less picturesque encrusting calcareous algae — one-celled plants — coat and bind together the coral to form a sturdy framework. The resulting coral-algal framework accounts for only about ⅓ of the reef's mass. The cavities in the reef structure are eventually filled with fragments of mollusk shells, **foraminifers** (carbonate-shelled one-celled animals), and pieces of branching calcareous algae. These fragments are also encrusted by carbonate-secreting algae and are incorporated into the reef.

Coral reefs are limited primarily to the Indian and Pacific Oceans lying near the equator (Fig. 2-5). In part this is a consequence of the

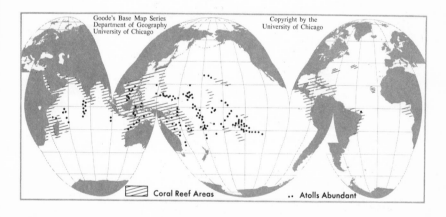

Fig. 2-5. Distribution of coral reefs and atolls.

corals' need for warm water. Most reef-building corals grow best in water with mean annual temperatures between 23° and 25°C and cannot tolerate prolonged exposures to cold or sudden large temperature changes. In addition, reefs require a foundation in the sunlit surface waters. The algae involved in secreting the carbonate that binds the reef together require sunlight.

Three different types of reef-associations commonly occur in the tropical oceans. **Fringing reefs** are connected to the land and grow parallel to the coast. They are generally absent near river mouths, probably killed by the fresh water from the rivers. Fringing reefs are usually rather narrow;

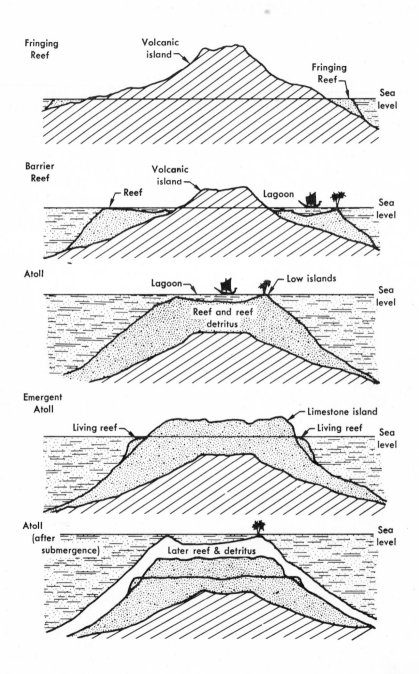

Fig. 2-6. Stages in the transition from Fringing Reef to Barrier Reef to Atoll. Later stages of emergence and submergence are shown.

widths range from a few tens to a few hundreds of meters. They border the large islands of the Hawaiian chain.

Barrier reefs are separated by shallow lagoons from the island or mainland. In general, they also tend to parallel the coast, with a few breaks through which ships may pass. The **Great Barrier Reef** along the northeast coast of Australia is the largest and most spectacular barrier reef. It extends about 2,500 km and is about 150 km wide.

Atolls consist of a lagoon, average depth about 50 m, surrounded by reefs with a few low carbonate-sand islands. No volcanic island remains above sea level. More than 300 atolls are known. Most occur in the western central Pacific Ocean; some occur in the Indian Ocean (Fig. 2-5). Only ten are found outside the tropical Indo-Pacific region.

More than a century ago, Charles Darwin observed the abundance of atolls in the western Pacific Ocean (Fig. 2-5) and deduced that atolls and fringing and barrier reefs around volcanic islands were part of an evolutionary series resulting from regional subsidence (Fig. 2-6). He hypothesized that fringing reefs around a volcanic island represented the first stage in atoll development. As the volcanic island slowly subsided, the reef continued to grow upward, forming a barrier reef with a lagoon separating it from the now smaller island. With further subsidence, the volcanic island would become smaller and eventually be submerged. But if the subsidence were slower than the rate at which the coral could grow upward, it could maintain itself at the sea surface as a reef. Finally, only a lagoon surrounded by the coral reef and a few islands built of carbonate sand would remain at the sea surface. Carbonate deposits would now fill the lagoon, burying any trace of the volcanic foundation.

During World War II, numerous flat-topped, deeply submerged sea-mounts, known as **guyots** or **tablemounts** (Fig. 2-7), were discovered in

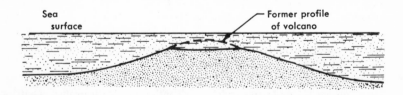

Fig. 2-7. Profile of tablemount and former profile of volcano before top was eroded off at the sea surface.

the western central Pacific Ocean near the abundant atolls. Their flat tops and the remains of coral-like shallow-water organisms dredged from them demonstrated that the tablemounts were once volcanic islands, whose wave-cut tops are now deeply submerged. These data led to the conclusion that large parts of the sea floor had indeed subsided many hundreds of meters. The subsidence of the sea floor and the absence of living coral reefs on many tablemounts in tropical oceans have not yet been satisfactorily explained.

Conclusive proof of Darwin's hypothesis came from drilling deep holes through the islands and reefs at Eniwetok Atoll in the Marshall Islands and Midway Island at the northwestern — and presumably oldest — end of the Hawaiian Islands. The deep holes encountered basaltic vocanic rock underlying the atolls, demonstrating that the atolls rested on volcanic foundations.

Darwin did not know of the changes of sea level caused by the Ice Ages. Had he known that the sea has stood between 100 and 200 m below its present level, he might have predicted some of the other features observed during those drilling operations. Each of the drilling operations encountered leached and recrystallized limestones containing shells of land snails. These limestones occur below the unaltered carbonate sediments and reefs now forming the atolls. The altered limestones apparently were formed when the older sediments were exposed above the sea during times of lower sea level (Fig. 2-6).

Other parts of the limestone caps beneath the atolls cannot be explained by lowered sea level during the Ice Ages. These limestones record several periods of emergence, millions of years before the last Ice Age began. Apparently the sea floor was elevated several times during a long period of net sinking. The sediments and limestone caps beneath the atoll thus record, rather indistinctly, changes in the ocean depth over a large part of the earth's surface.

QUESTIONS

1. Compare the ocean boundaries (Fig. 1-2) with the deep-ocean topography (Fig. 2-4). Which of the ocean boundaries most closely corresponds to the submerged topographic features? Which do not correspond? Where would you draw the ocean boundaries considering the ocean-floor topography?

2. What sea-floor features are included as part of the continental margins?

3. Which sea-floor features are included as part of the ocean-basin floor?

4. What is the significance of the nearly horizontal portions of the hypsometric curve? Of the steeply sloping parts?

5. What effect might the mid-ocean rises have on oceanic circulation?

6. Using an echo-sounder which gives a continuous depth profile, what topographic features would be useful to identify a submarine volcano?

7. Briefly describe and compare the structure and composition of the ocean basins and the continental blocks.

8. List the conditions necessary for the growth of reef-building corals.

9. What type of evidence could be used to prove that tablemounts (guyots) were once at the sea surface?

10. On a world globe (radius 35 cm) how thick would the average ocean be? What would be the maximum relief? (Assume that the trenches are 11,000 m deep, that Mt. Everest is 8,800 m high.)

SUPPLEMENTARY READING

Dietz, R. S., "The Pacific Floor," *Scientific American,* April, 1952.

Fairbridge, R. W., "The Changing Level of the Sea," *Scientific American,* May, 1960.

Fisher, R. L., and R. Revelle, "The Trenches of the Pacific," *Scientific American,* November, 1955.

Heezen, Bruce C., "The Origin of Submarine Canyons," *Scientific American,* August, 1956.

————, "The Rift in the Ocean Floor," *Scientific American,* October, 1960.

Menard, H. W., "The East Pacific Rise," *Scientific American,* December, 1961.

————, "Fractures in the Pacific Floor," *Scientific American,* July, 1955.

Shepard, Francis P., *The Earth Beneath the Sea.* Baltimore: The Johns Hopkins Press, 1959. Elementary.

Stetson, H. C., "The Continental Shelf," *Scientific American,* March, 1955.

Chapter 3

Deep-Sea Sediment

Except for relatively few areas of exposed rock, the ocean floor is carpeted with sediment. These deposits consist of insoluble particles from the continents, mixed with the undissolved shells and skeletal remains of marine organisms. Study of these deposits has provided important clues to the processes affecting the ocean today. In addition, deep-sea sediments contain a record of earth history extending over the past 100 million years, of which relatively little has been sampled or studied by geologists. Common sampling devices only recover material from the sediment surface (Fig. 3-1) or penetrate a few meters or tens of meters below that surface (Fig. 3-2).

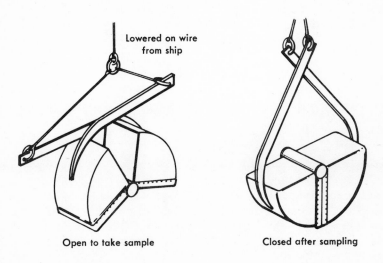

Lowered on wire
from ship

Open to take sample   Closed after sampling

Fig. 3-1. **Van Veen sampler used to obtain sediment samples from the shallow-ocean bottom.**

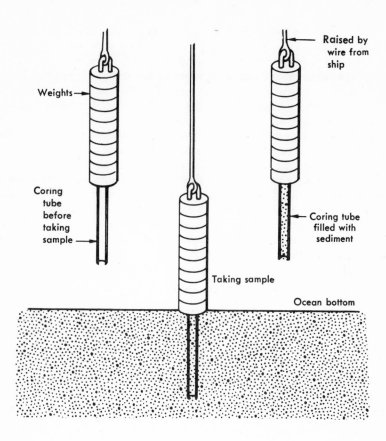

Weights

Coring
tube
before
taking
sample

Raised by
wire from
ship

Coring tube
filled with
sediment

Taking sample

Ocean bottom

Fig. 3-2. Gravity-operated device used to obtain a sediment core from the ocean bottom.

Using the reflection and refraction (bending) of waves from earthquakes and man-made explosions, geophysicists have studied the structure of the ocean bottom. These data show that sediment thickness varies widely, even within one ocean. In the Pacific Ocean, the thickness of the uncompacted sediment is about 600 m or less. In the Atlantic Ocean it varies between 500 and 1,000 m. In the Puerto Rico Trench, the sediment thickness exceeds 9 km, and in parts of the Arctic Sea it exceeds 4 km. For our purposes, we will assume that the average thickness of uncompacted sediment in the deep ocean is 600 m.

Deep-sea sediment commonly contains 50 per cent water. Thus if we were to compact these sediments, squeezing out the water, the compacted sediment would form a layer only 300 m thick.

CLASSIFICATION OF SEDIMENT AND SEDIMENTARY PARTICLES

Various sediment properties may be studied. Particle size, origin, or color, as well as texture or geometry of the sediment deposit, can provide information to supplement that derived from other techniques. We will consider how data on the size and origin of the sediment particles can be used to study sediment sources and modes of transport. In addition, we will consider certain interactions with sea water which modify sediment properties, such as color or mineral composition.

Size of the sediment particles, or grains, is easily determined; the loose sediment may be washed through sieves with progressively smaller openings. By weighing the amount retained on each sieve, the grain size distribution is determined. Another common technique is to determine the abundance of particles remaining suspended in water at various times after the sediment-water mixture is shaken. With these techniques one determines the relative amount of **sand** (grains larger than 62 microns* in diameter) and **mud** (grains smaller than 62 microns in diameter) present in a sediment sample.

Table 3-1.   Average Composition of Deep-Sea Sediment*

| Constituent | Brown mud (%) | Calcareous mud (%) | Siliceous muds | |
			Diatomaceous mud (%)	Radiolarian mud (%)
Biogenous				
Calcareous	8	65	7	4
Siliceous	1	2	70	54
Lithogenous				
(& Hydrogenous)	91	33	23	42

*Recalculated after R. R. Revelle, "Marine bottom sediment collected in the Pacific Ocean by the *Carnegie* on its Seventh Cruise," *Carnegie Institution Washington Publ.* 556, part 1 (1944) 180 p.

In general, sands are deposited on the continental shelf and commonly occur along the shore, forming beaches. Sands may also occur in irregular patches at greater depths on the continental shelf. Their occurrence may be the result of some now-inactive geological process or former ocean condition. Such sediments are known as **relict sediments** because they were not deposited by processes now active. For example, many continental shelves have sand on their outer edge which may be the result of sand deposition, perhaps on ancient beaches formed when the sea stood at a lower level. After sea level rose, the sands in these areas have not been removed or buried by later sediment accumulations.

Mud is the most common sediment covering the deep-ocean floor (Fig. 3-3), as well as the continental shelf and slope. In the deep-sea

---

*See Appendix for definition.

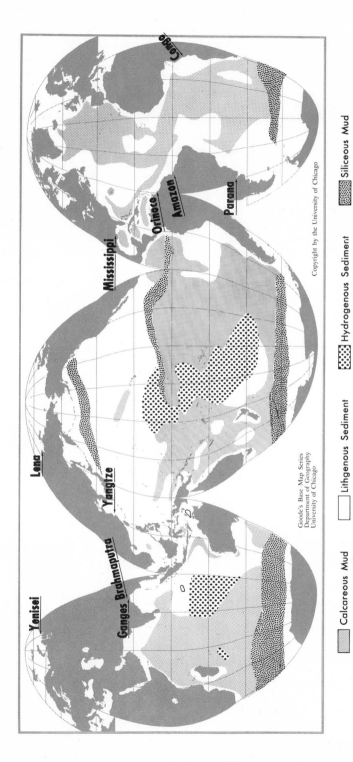

Fig. 3-3. Distribution of deep-sea sediments. The mouths of the ten largest rivers are shown. (Modified after G. Arrhenius, "Pelagic Sediments," in The Sea: Ideas and Observations on Progress in the Study of the Seas, vol. 3, ed. M. N. Hill [New York: Interscience Publishers, 1963] p. 657.)

Goode's Base Map Series
Department of Geography
University of Chicago

Copyright by the University of Chicago

Calcareous Mud   Lithgenous Sediment   Hydrogenous Sediment   Siliceous Mud

31

sediments, sand-sized particles generally constitute less than 10 per cent of the sediment. Deep-sea sediments consisting of 30 per cent or more of the skeletons or shells of marine organisms have been called **oozes.** In the North Atlantic Ocean, approximately 20 per cent of the deep-sea sediment samples contain sand layers, thought to have been deposited by the sediment-laden **turbidity currents.** These are discussed in a later section of this chapter.

Although determining the origin of particles is frequently more difficult than determining grain size, such knowledge is useful to distinguish different sediments and to locate their sources (Table 3-1). Sediment particles may be classified according to origin as follows:

1. **Lithogenous** (derived from rocks) **components** are primarily mineral grains derived from soils formed on the continents and transported to the ocean by rivers or the wind. Volcanoes on the land or under the sea also contribute lithogenous particles such as volcanic ash.

2. **Biogenous** (derived from organisms) **components** are skeletal remains, such as shells, bones, and teeth of marine organisms. They may contribute calcium carbonate, silica (opal) or phosphate minerals to the sediment.

3. **Hydrogenous** (derived from water) **components** originate from inorganic chemical reactions in sea water or in the sediment itself. An example is manganese nodules.

LITHOGENOUS SEDIMENT

Lithogenous sediment is composed primarily of the mineral grains brought into the oceans by rivers. The sediment particles are derived from the breakdown of rocks during soil formation on the continents. When the soil particles are carried by running water into rivers and transported to the oceans, we call the process **erosion.** Rivers carry small particles suspended in the water. Larger grains, usually sand-sized, are dragged along the bottom by the river flow.

Eventually the particles are deposited, when the water movements are too weak to move the grains. On the continental shelf, wave action or currents may sort the sediment particles by size, depositing the large particles and removing the smallest particles. The largest particles tend to remain near the shore, where they may form beaches. Smaller particles are commonly transported seaward and deposited in deeper water on the continental shelf and slope. These tiny particles may also be carried by the ocean surface currents or moved by the near-bottom currents. The resulting fine-grained sediments, usually muds, are frequently deposited in bands more or less parallel to the coastline.

Despite the movement of the sediment particles after reaching the ocean, most do not travel far. Thus a large fraction of the sediment brought to the ocean by a river tends to be deposited near its mouth. Indeed it appears that *most lithogenous sediment does not travel beyond the continental shelf and slope.*

Some very small particles are carried away from the continents by water movement. Such minute particles may take several years to settle to the ocean bottom. Particles less than 0.5 microns in diameter may take several hundred years to pass through the oceans and reach the bottom. During this time the particles may be carried thousands of kilometers by ocean currents. Hence virtually every part of the ocean receives some lithogenous sediment. Far from the continents, the lithogenous sediment accumulates slowly, forming a layer approximately 1 mm thick in a thousand to ten thousand years. Near the continents, and especially near large rivers such as the Amazon or Congo rivers, lithogenous sediment accumulates much more rapidly.

The long transit time of very small particles in the ocean not only results in their wide dispersal, but also provides ample opportunity for chemical reactions to take place. For example, iron in the water or on the particle can react with the dissolved oxygen in sea water, forming a rust-like iron oxide coating on mineral grains. The abundance of such red- or brown-stained grains in deep-sea sediment accounts for their colors and their names, red-clay, **brown mud.** Colors of deep-sea sediments range from brick red in the Atlantic to chocolate brown in the Pacific Ocean.

In contrast, rapidly accumulating sediment on the continental shelf and slope may be in contact with the sea water for too short a period to react fully with the dissolved oxygen in the water. Thus these grains do not commonly acquire a reddish or brownish color. Such sediments have a variety of colors and are often referred to as green muds or blue muds. Green and blue colors are especially conspicuous in sediments accumulating in areas overlain by ocean waters having unusually low dissolved-oxygen contents.

Some lithogenous particles are transported by winds and enter the ocean through the surface layers. This is especially important in the two east-west belts centered around 30°N and 30°S. High mountains and the world's deserts are a prime source for air-borne dust particles. Where the influx of lithogenous grains from rivers is low, air-borne particles may be locally an important source of sediment.

Fine-grained volcanic ash blown into the atmosphere during volcanic eruptions settles out on the adjacent ocean surface. The volcanic ash particles are incorporated in the deep-sea sediment, often very near the volcanic area, such as the Indonesian or Aleutian areas. The mineral grains and volcanic rock fragments are often easily recognized in the sediments. Under favorable conditions, volcanic fragments or layers of ash from known large volcanic eruptions can be identified in the surface sediments.

Of the estimated 10,000 volcanoes on the ocean floor, only a few, such as those forming the Hawaiian Islands, penetrate the ocean surface to form islands. It seems likely, however, that eruptions of submarine volcanoes contribute large amounts of lithogenous sediment to the ocean floor. Because of the difficulty of observing these volcanic eruptions, our knowledge of their sediment contribution and other effects remains limited.

Glaciers, thick sheets of ice on land, are another source of lithogenous sediment. As glaciers flow from the interior to the coast, the underlying rock surfaces are worn down with the removal of fine rock fragments, sometimes called glacial flour. In addition, the ice picks up and carries rocks and boulders of various sizes. When the glacier flows into the ocean, blocks of ice break off, forming icebergs. As they melt, the icebergs release their sediment load. The resulting **glacial-marine sediment** — a mixture of mud, sand, and boulders deposited in the ocean — covers much of the Antarctic continental shelf and some of the North Pacific deep-sea floor.

During the most recent Ice Age, which ended about 10,000 years ago, large parts of the Northern Hemisphere continents were covered by continental glaciers, much as Antarctica is presently. It is not surprising that the adjacent continental shelves were covered by glacial-marine sediment. Continental shelf areas off formerly glaciated coasts often do not receive sufficient modern sediment to bury these relict sediments, leaving them exposed at the surface. The continental shelf off the New England coast of the United States is covered by such relict sediments.

TURBIDITY CURRENTS

Before 1950, most oceanographers and geologists believed that deep-sea deposits accumulated only by the particle-by-particle deposition of individual grains settling slowly through the oceans. In the mid-1950's, investigations of submarine telegraph cable breaks associated with earthquakes in many parts of the world indicated that currents of relatively dense, mud-rich water, called **turbidity currents,** flow down the continental slope and onto the ocean floor. Such flows, actually observed in Lake Mead, on the Colorado River, and in certain European lakes, can transport sandy sediment originally deposited on the continental shelf or slope onto the deep-sea floor.

Data on the time elapsed between the earthquakes and the breaking of the cables indicate that turbidity currents can travel at speeds greater than 20 km/hour (approximately equivalent to 12 miles per hour). Submarine cable breaks, presumably caused by turbidity currents, are common near major rivers, such as the Congo River, which carry large amounts of sediment into the ocean. Although occurring intermittently, such flows appear to be a major factor in the transportation and deposition of sediment over large areas of the ocean floor. A turbidity current in 1929, caused by an earthquake on the Grand Banks south of Newfoundland, is thought to have deposited sediment on the deep ocean floor over an area about 1,000 km long and 100 to 300 km wide.

Although such large turbidity currents have not been observed directly, most oceanographers and marine geologists believe them to be an important sediment-transporting agency in the deep ocean. Such flows explain the common occurrence of **turbidities** — displaced sands with unusual textures, containing abundant shells and other remains of shallow water organisms, interbedded with deep-sea sediment. Turbidity currents appear to be a major factor in forming and in removing the sediment deposited in submarine canyons. Canyons near the mouths of large, sediment-laden rivers would soon fill up if they were not occasionally emptied.

Such sediment-rich flows are much more dense than normal sea water because of their suspended sediment load. The dense mud-water mixture thus sinks and flows along the ocean bottom. It appears that turbidity currents often flow along channels on the ocean bottom, much as a large river does on land.

Obstructions on the bottom can deflect turbidity currents and even prevent their escape onto the deep-ocean floor. This is especially obvious in the Pacific, where the many island arcs and trenches prevent some of the turbidity currents from flowing out onto the adjacent ocean floor (Fig. 2-3). In the Atlantic, Indian, and Arctic Oceans, turbidity currents can flow over much of the sea floor, covering the preexisting topography with thick blankets of sediment and forming the large, rather featureless plains. Tops of seamounts, submarine ridges and banks are usually not affected by turbidity currents. There sediment accumulates by the particle-by-particle deposition of individual grains.

BIOGENOUS SEDIMENT

Undissolved skeletal remains of organisms are important constituents of certain deep-sea sediments. These **biogenous constituents** may be divided into three major groups, based primarily on their chemical composition and secondarily on the organisms from which they are derived. Listed here in order of abundance they are:

Calcareous constituents (Fig. 3-4), primarily calcium carbonate, are derived from shells of **foraminifers** (a family of one-celled animals), **coccoliths** (platelets secreted by tiny, one-celled algae, the *Coccolithophoridea*), and, rarely, the shells of tiny, floating snails.

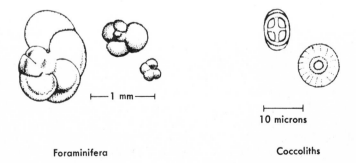

|—1 mm—|

|————————|
10 microns

Foraminifera   Coccoliths

Fig. 3-4. Some calcareous constituents of deep-sea sediments.

Siliceous constituents (Fig. 3-5) are primarily **opal,** the hydrated silica $(SiO_2 \cdot H_2O)$ derived principally from shells of **diatoms** (one-celled algae), and **radiolaria** (one-celled animals).

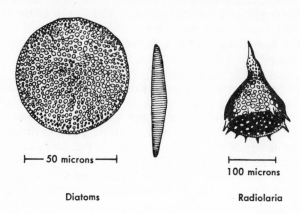

├── 50 microns ──┤

├────────────┤
100 microns

Diatoms   Radiolaria

Fig. 3-5.   **Some siliceous constituents of deep-sea sediments.**

Phosphatic constituents (rich in phosphate) are derived primarily from the bones, teeth, and scales of fish and other marine vertebrates. Areas such as offshore banks where fish are abundant may be covered by sediment composed in large part of such skeletal debris.

We consider as biogenous sediment (or **ooze**) any deposit containing more than 30 per cent biogenous constituents by volume. Most deep-sea sediments being muds, we have then **calcareous muds** and **siliceous muds.** Muds rich in phosphate are rare in the deep sea, although they are sometimes found covering submarine ridges or banks. Calcareous muds cover nearly half of the deep-sea floor and are most abundant on the shallower parts (less than 4,500 m) of the ocean floor. They accumulate at rates between one and four centimeters per thousand years. Siliceous muds occur principally in the Pacific Ocean, where their presence is not masked by large amounts of lithogenous sediment. Diatom-rich muds nearly surround Antarctica and occur in the North Pacific Ocean; radiolaria-rich sediment occurs in the equatorial Pacific.

In our discussion of lithogenous sediment we considered only the source and transportation of the sediment particles. When we discuss biogenous sediment, we must consider not only the source — generally **production** by organisms living in the sunlit waters near the ocean surface — but also the **destruction** of the biogenous particles. Marine organisms are able to remove from sea water the materials they require for skeleton formation (silicate, calcium, phosphorus). Organisms forming siliceous or phosphatic skeletons must remove these elements from large volumes of water, where they occur in extremely low concentrations.

Most organisms are eventually eaten and their skeletons or shells broken into smaller pieces. As these pieces sink to the ocean floor, they tend to dissolve, causing the disappearance of the more soluble shells. For calcareous shells, dissolution is most rapid in deeper ocean waters and on the deeper ocean floor. Siliceous and phosphatic remains apparently dissolve at all depths. The longer the skeletal fragments are in contact with ocean water, the more completely they are dissolved and removed. This may occur as the fragments sink through the water or after they fall to the bottom but remain unburied by later sediment accumulations. After burial, the skeletal fragments are nearly isolated from the overlying sea water, and their rate of dissolution is greatly reduced.

Consequently, certain organisms may be found living in profusion in water near the ocean surface, but rarely, if ever, observed in deep-sea sediment. Thus a potentially important source of sediment may be partially or completely obscured by destruction of the biogenous constituents before and immediately following deposition.

Another factor to be considered is **dilution.** Since by definition a biogenous sediment must contain more than 30 per cent biogenous constituents, it is evident that if lithogenous particles are supplied in large amounts, the proportion of biogenous material may never be high enough to form a biogenous sediment.

In summary, *the distribution of biogenous sediment is controlled by production, destruction, and dilution.* The present distribution of biogenous sediment represents a balance between various oceanic processes. From studies of the distribution of biogenous sediment on and below the deep-ocean floor, oceanographers hope to decipher some of the interactions between sediment particles and sea water.

HYDROGENOUS SEDIMENT

Manganese nodules, black, potato-sized nodules, or sometimes larger slabs, composed of a complex mixture of iron-manganese minerals, occur at the sediment surface over much of the ocean floor. Photographs of the deep-sea floor indicate that the nodules cover 20 to 50 per cent of the Pacific Ocean bottom. Although analogous deposits are known on land, manganese nodules are one of the most distinctive constituents of deep-sea deposits. Many details of their origin and mineral composition remain unknown. Most geochemists who have studied them agree that they form extremely slowly; a layer a few hundredths of a millimeter to a millimeter thick forming in a thousand years. Viewed on the atomic level, this corresponds to between one and one hundred atomic layers per day, one of the slowest chemical reactions known.

Because of its exceedingly slow rate of accumulation, hydrogenous sediment is abundant only in ocean areas remote from major rivers and where biogenous constituents are scarce. In other areas, lithogenous or biogenous constituents dominate the sediment formed. For example, in the central Pacific Ocean, the belt of hydrogenous sediment is interrupted by radiolarian-rich siliceous muds near the equator (Fig. 3-3). This does not mean that hydrogenous constituents do not form in areas of rapidly accumulating sediments. Instead of forming large nodules or slabs at the surface, they may occur as small, pea-sized or smaller, micronodules embedded in the more abundant constituents.

MINERAL RESOURCES FROM THE SEA FLOOR

Because of their vast expanse, the deposits on the sea floor would logically seem to offer an important source of useful minerals and materials. Thus far, however, the sea floor has yielded only a meager harvest. Most mineral resources now exploited lie in shallow water along the continental margins. Many are simply the seaward extension of valuable deposits well known and exploited on the adjacent land.

Petroleum and natural gas are by far the most valuable commodities now obtained from the continental shelf in many parts of the world. Less important overall is the production of sulfur, coal and iron. In each case these deposits are known on land but extend beneath the adjacent ocean.

Ancient beaches, now submerged on the continental shelf, are the source of valuable materials in certain areas. Among the minerals recovered are gold off Alaska, and diamonds off Southwest Africa. In the future, these ancient beaches may also supply sand to nearby resort beaches. This is likely to be especially important where the natural sand supply has been affected by man's modification of the coastal sand regime.

Submerged river channels provide local sources of platinum off Alaska, and tin off Thailand and Indonesia. Lime-poor islands and coastal areas use carbonate shell sands for the manufacture of cement.

Two materials, phosphorite and manganese nodules, derived from the sea floor itself, seem to hold some promise as future economic resources. One scheme to recover phosphate rock from shallow banks off Southern California was abandoned. The area containing the deposit had previously served as a dumping ground for naval ammunition and as a target practice area; the live torpedoes and large naval shells proved too great a hazard. With the increasing need for phosphate to be used in fertilizer, other sea floor areas may be worked in the future.

Manganese nodules may also prove to be economically important. Locally present in great abundance, the nodules are a possible source of iron, manganese, copper, cobalt and nickel.

QUESTIONS

1. List three processes transporting lithogenous sediment into the deep ocean. Which is most important? Which is least important? Why?
2. Why are calcareous muds so widespread in the South Pacific Ocean and so rare in the North Pacific Ocean?
3. What type of sediment is being deposited in the Arctic Sea? Why?
4. What distinguishes a biogenous sediment from a lithogenous sediment?
5. List the factors controlling the distribution of biogenous sediment. Which is most important? Which is least important?
6. List the major organisms actively supplying biogenous sediment to the deep-ocean floor. Indicate their relative importance.
7. Describe the distribution of sand and mud on the ocean floor.
8. Define turbidity currents and discuss the evidence for their existence.

9. Which ocean has the greatest abundance of hydrogenous deposits? Which has the least? Why?
10. Why are fish bones seldom recognizable in deep-sea sediments?
11. Where are the possible sources for the manganese and iron deposited in manganese nodules?

SUPPLEMENTARY READING

Kuenen, P. H., "Sand," *Scientific American,* April, 1960.

Mero, J. L., "Minerals on the Ocean Floor," *Scientific American,* December, 1960.

Shepard, Francis P., *The Earth Beneath the Sea.* Baltimore: The Johns Hopkins Press, 1959. Nontechnical.

_____, *Submarine Geology.* Second edition. New York: Harper and Row, Publishers, 1963. Technical, good bibliography.

Chapter 4

Water and Its Properties

Water is not only the most abundant substance in the oceans, but its properties have a profound influence on the surface of the entire earth and the existence of life as we know it. It will be useful to separate our discussion of sea water into two parts: pure water (this chapter) and sea water as a salt solution (Chapter 5).

WATER MOLECULES AND THEIR INTERACTIONS

The water molecule consists of an oxygen atom bonded to two hydrogen atoms. Because of the configuration of the oxygen atom's electron

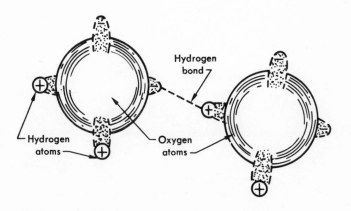

Fig. 4-1. Two water molecules showing the basic four-cornered structure of each. The molecules are shown linked by a hydrogen bond, an interaction between one of the hydrogen atoms of one molecule and a negative charge on the other water molecule.

cloud, the two hydrogen atoms in the water molecule are situated at an angle of approximately 105° and located at two corners of a basically four-cornered molecule (Fig. 4-1). If we could examine a single water molecule, we would see two positive charges, the hydrogen atoms, on the side. Each hydrogen atom shares its single electron with the oxygen atom and thus acts as a positive charge on the exterior of the water molecule. From the opposite side we would see only the oxygen atom, which because of the shared electrons appears to have excess negative charges. Hence the charges on a water molecule are separated. Molecules with such separated charges are known as **polar molecules.**

Regardless of their structure, all molecules have a weak attraction for each other. These forces, called the **van der Waals forces,** arise from interactions between the atomic nuclei of one molecule and the electrons of another molecule. Such forces become significant only when the interacting molecules are very close together.

The pronounced separation of the charges and the presence of hydrogen atoms in the water molecules gives rise to a much stronger type of interaction — the formation of **hydrogen bonds.** Many of water's anomalous properties are a consequence of the formation of hydrogen bonds between adjacent molecules.

Hydrogen bonds are only about ¹⁄₂₀ as strong as the bonds between hydrogen and oxygen within the water molecule itself. Nonetheless they are strong enough to influence greatly the structural properties of liquid water. If hydrogen bonding were not present, the melting point of ice would be approximately $-100°C$, and the boiling point of water approximately $-80°C$. In other words, water would occur as a gas at the temperatures and atmospheric pressures of the earth's surface. Without the hydrogen bonding of water molecules we would have no oceans on earth, or life as we know it.

FORMS OF WATER

Water is one of the few common substances that exists at the earth's surface in all three **forms of matter: crystalline solid** — ice, **liquid** — water, and **gas** — water vapor. We will consider each of these to see how their structure controls their properties and to understand better the influence of the properties of water on the oceans.

Like all crystalline solids, ice has an orderly internal structure. The hexagonal (six-sided) crystals of ice may be seen in snowflakes. The external shape of ice crystals such as snowflakes is a manifestation of the fixed positions of the molecules in the ice structure.

If we could see the ice structure on an atomic scale (Fig. 4-2), we would find that each molecule is bound so that it can neither move nor rotate freely. The intermolecular bonds are somewhat elastic like springs, permitting vibrations but greatly inhibiting long-range movements of the molecules. The bonds formed by individual water molecules extend in four directions (Fig. 4-1). Other water molecules are located along each bond

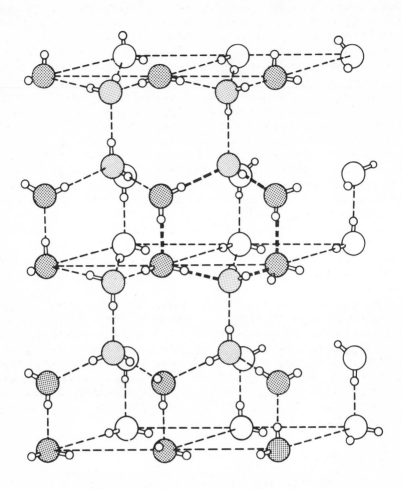

Fig. 4-2. Crystal structure of ice. Note the six-sided rings formed by the water molecules. (After Theodore Brown, *General Chemistry* [Columbus, Ohio: Charles E. Merrill Books, Inc., 1963] p. 128.)

direction. The hydrogen-bonded molecules form an interconnected framework extending in three dimensions. Because of the fixed directions of the bonds, the ice structure is a rather open network of water molecules. Molecules in the ice network are not as closely packed as a similar number of randomly packed molecules fitted together like marbles in a cup. Consequently, ice at 0°C has a relatively low density, approximately 0.92 gram per cubic centimeter. Liquid water at the same temperature has a density of nearly one gram per cubic centimeter. Hence ordinary ice floats on water because a piece of ice weighs less than an equal volume of water.

Despite the openness of the ice structure, it is difficult to fit impurities, such as sea salts, into it. The salt atoms or molecules do not readily fit into the small holes in the ice structure, nor do they substitute readily for water molecules in the ice structure. Thus, most sea salts are excluded from sea ice formed by freezing sea water. The salt remains behind in the unfrozen water. Also some salty water remains as brine inclusions in the newly formed sea ice. With time the brine inclusions migrate through the blocks of sea ice and are eventually expelled from the ice. As a result, old sea ice contains much less salt than newly formed sea ice.

It is common knowledge that when ice melts, liquid water forms. From observing the disappearance of ice crystals during melting, we might have expected that all the intermolecular bonds, responsible for the ice structure, would also have disappeared. Instead, many water molecules remain bound together in ice-like clusters (Fig. 4-3) surrounded by unbonded water molecules. As a result, water is a highly atypical liquid. In fact, we may consider liquid water to be a pseudo-crystalline substance in the low temperature range involved in the oceans. This is a direct consequence of the strong tendency of water molecules to form hydrogen bonds. At low temperatures many of the molecules in liquid water are loosely organized into clusters at any instant (Fig. 4-4). The proportion of bonded molecules and the relative size of the ice-like clusters decreases as the temperature of the water rises.

Obviously, liquid water does not behave like ice; it flows readily, maintaining only a fixed volume at a given temperature. Water's ability to flow is due, in part, to the fact that some water molecules are not bound but can move and rotate freely. These unbound water molecules apparently form one or two layers of closely packed molecules around

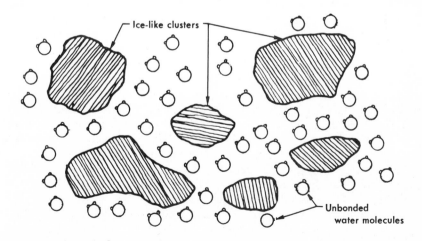

Fig. 4-3. Schematic representation of the liquid-water structure. (After R. A. Horne, "The Physical Chemistry and Structure of Sea Water," *Water Resources Research*, 1 [1965], 269.)

the ice-like clusters (Fig. 4-4). They can move or rotate with little or
no restriction.

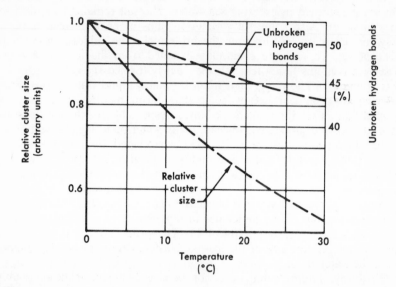

Fig. 4-4. Effect of temperature on the relative number of unbroken hydrogen
bonds and the relative cluster size in pure water. (Data from G. Nemethy and
H. A. Scheraga, "Structure of Water and Hydrophobic Bonding in Protein,"
Journal of Chemical Physics **36** [1962] 3394.)

The structure of liquid water is far from static. Molecules change
rapidly between the two components. In liquid water the intermolecular
bonds which cause the ice-like clusters to hold together, apparently break
up and reform about 10^{12} (a million million) times each second. In ice
the bonds persist much longer, breaking about once a second.

The relative abundance of the structured and unstructured components
of water can be changed by varying temperature, pressure, or salt content.
The rapid changes or "flickering" of the structure account for water's
ability to flow. If the structure did not rapidly break and reform, water
would be as rigid or brittle as ice, fracturing instead of flowing.

Water vapor, a gas, has neither shape nor size, but will completely
fill any container in which it is placed. To change from liquid water to
water vapor, all the intermolecular bonds must be broken. Individual
molecules may then move and rotate independently of each other and have
little interaction. On a molecular level, water vapor in a container has been
compared to a room full of angry bees. Each bee, representing a single
molecule, can move independently and is little influenced by the other bees.

The **pressure** exerted by a gas on its container is represented by the
molecules colliding with the walls. As the temperature increases, the mole-

cules move more rapidly, colliding with the walls more frequently. Hence, the pressure increases with a rise in temperature. In a vapor there is so much space between the individual molecules that we can add other gases with little difficulty, although the total pressure of the gas mixture increases when we do this.

DENSITY

Density — mass per unit volume — is one of the most important properties to be considered for substances in the ocean. A substance denser than water sinks. Conversely, a substance less dense than water floats at the surface. In this respect, the oceans behave much like the atmosphere, and the same principles governing vertical stability are applicable.

Let us first consider the density of ice. Because of the relatively open structure of ice, it is approximately 9 per cent less dense than water at 0°C. Consequently, ice floats on water, one of the few common solids to float in its own liquid.

Temperature influences the density of ice; it becomes steadily less dense as temperature increases (Fig. 4-5). This is true of most substances. Viewed in another way, the same mass of material occupies more volume when heated, thereby reducing the density. The increased volume results from the increased vibrations of the individual molecules or atoms

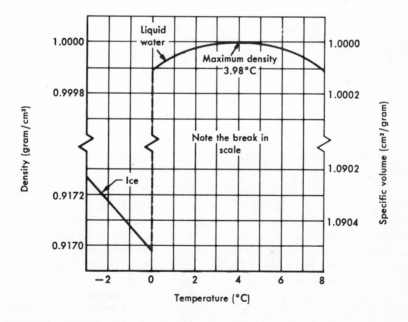

Fig. 4-5. Effect of temperature on density (grams/cubic centimeter) and specific volume (cubic centimeters/gram) of ice and pure liquid water.

as the temperature is increased. Warm air, for instance, is less dense than cold air; consequently it rises.

The density of liquid water varies as a result of changes in temperature and pressure. The unusual density changes caused by temperature variations illustrate the importance of the hydrogen-bonded structure on water properties.

If we take one gram of pure water at room temperature, say 20°C, and cool it, we find that at first the water occupies progressively less volume as the temperature decreases (Fig. 4-5). The decrease in volume continues until our gram of water occupies exactly 1 cubic centimeter at approximately 4°C, the **temperature of maximum density.** Instead of continuing to shrink as we would expect, it expands slightly until it begins to freeze at 0°C. This anomalous behavior is apparently a consequence of the structure of liquid water.

In water at temperatures above 4°C, the reduction in volume (or increase in density) with decreasing temperature is due primarily to the diminished thermal agitation of the water molecules. Each unbonded water molecule occupies less volume as the temperature is lowered. However, near the freezing point, this reduction in the volume of the unbonded water molecules is not sufficient to compensate for the increase in abundance of the more bulky ice-like clusters (Fig. 4-3). As the clusters become more abundant near the freezing point, they cause the anomalous low-temperature increase in volume below about 4°C.

Briefly, the density maximum at about 4°C is a direct consequence of water's hydrogen-bonded structure. The temperature of maximum density can be lowered by increasing the pressure or by adding salt. Either of these inhibits the formation of the ice-like clusters.

The density maximum of pure water plays an important role in the behavior of fresh-water lakes in cold regions. The most dense water formed in such lakes during the winter will have a temperature around 4°C. This water will fill the deeper parts of the lake. Colder water and ice will float at the surface.

THERMAL PROPERTIES AND CHANGES OF STATE

Changes in the physical form of a substance, such as a solid changing to a liquid to a vapor, are known as **changes of state.** As can be seen from our discussion of the different structures of water, a change of state requires the breaking or forming of bonds between molecules. If bonds are broken, energy must be supplied to break them. If new bonds are formed during the change of state, energy is released. This energy is normally supplied or released in the form of heat.

We need to introduce a measure of heat, the **calorie,** so that we can describe exactly the amount of heat we add to a given amount of matter. For our purposes we will define the calorie as the amount of heat (or energy) required to raise the temperature of one gram of liquid water by one degree Celsius. For example, 100 calories of heat must be supplied to one gram of water to change its temperature from the melting point (0°C) to the boiling point (100°C).

Let us take one gram of ice and add heat to it (Fig. 4-6). This will

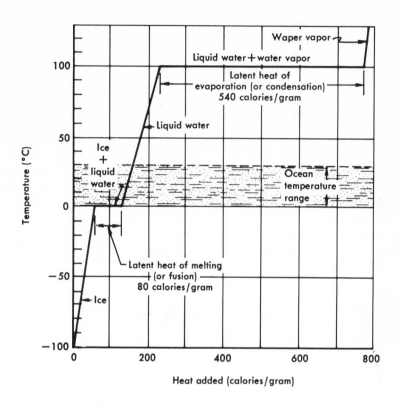

Fig. 4-6. Changes in temperature when heat is added (or removed) from ice, liquid water, or water vapor. Note that the temperature does not change when mixtures of ice and liquid water or liquid water and water vapor are present.

illustrate the relationship between the addition of heat and changes in temperature as well as changes of state in our water system. As we know, the water molecules in the ice structure (or lattice) can vibrate because the molecular bonds are somewhat elastic. As we add heat to ice, the additional energy causes the molecular vibrations to become stronger, causing the molecular bonds to stretch slightly. We experience the increased molecular vibrations as a rise in temperature.

At the melting point of ice (0°C), the molecular vibrations are strong enough to permit a large number of the molecules to break loose from the ice structure, forming liquid water. If we momentarily stop adding heat to the system, ice and liquid water will exist together in **equilibrium**. At equilibrium, the number of molecules gaining enough energy to break free of the ice structure at any instant is balanced by the number of water molecules losing energy and rejoining the ice structure. Unless we add or remove energy, the relative amount of ice and liquid water remains fixed.

Adding more heat causes the melting of more ice. Removing heat through cooling would have the opposite effect. As long as we have ice and water together, adding more heat does not change the temperature of our system. Instead, the added energy is used to break more bonds in the ice structure, causing melting. After we have added enough heat, approximately 80 calories per gram, the last bit of ice disappears. The amount of heat necessary to melt a gram of ice at 0°C is called the **latent heat of melting**. The heat consumed is again released when the water freezes — hence the term **latent heat**.

When the last bit of ice disappears, additional heating of the system causes a rise in temperature. The energy, no longer entirely used up in breaking bonds, causes the water molecules to move more rapidly. Again we experience the more rapid molecular movement as a rise in temperature. Between the melting point and the boiling point, the addition of a fixed amount of heat causes a nearly constant rise in temperature. This relationship between the amount of heat supplied and the resulting temperature change is known as the **heat capacity** of a substance. (We used this relationship to define the calorie.) Because of its structure, several times as much heat must be supplied to water to cause a 1°C rise in temperature than is necessary to cause a 1°C rise in temperature of a common granitic or basaltic rock of equal mass. (We notice this effect on a summer day at the beach. The ground becomes hot during the day, cooling noticably at night, whereas the water temperature changes very little over a 24 hour period.) The heat capacity of liquid water is unusually high for a liquid because of water's pseudo-crystalline structure. Water in the ocean therefore can absorb or release large amounts of energy as heat and yet change its temperature very little.

When liquid water reaches 100°C, its boiling point, the molecules acquire sufficient energy to break free of the liquid water structure, forming water vapor, a gas. A relatively large amount of heat energy, 539 calories per gram, is required to evaporate water at 100°C. The reason for this is easy to understand. When water evaporates, the hydrogen-bonded ice-like clusters are completely broken up. Because of the strength of the hydrogen bond, this requires much energy (Fig. 4-6). Hence, the **latent heat of evaporation** for water is very large.

In contrast the latent heat of melting for water at 0°C is only 80 calories. Here the ice structure is not completely destroyed; all the hydrogen bonds are not broken (Fig. 4-4). Consequently, melting ice requires much less energy than evaporating water.

Even though water boils at 100°C, forming water vapor, we must not overlook the fact that water vapor can form from either ice or liquid water at much lower temperatures. For example, wet clothes can dry even when completely frozen.

Some of the water molecules in ice or liquid water gain enough energy to break their bonds and escape, forming water vapor. Evaporation from the sea surface is extremely important for the earth's heat and water budgets. Obviously this occurs well below the boiling point; the mean sea surface temperature is approximately 18°C.

Evaporation of water below the boiling point requires more heat per gram of water vapor than evaporation at the boiling point. The increase

Temperature	Latent heat of evaporation (cal/gram)
0°	595
20°	585
100°	539

in the latent heat of evaporation represents the extra work that must be done to break the hydrogen bonds at these lower temperatures.

It is also important to realize that these processes — or changes of state — are reversible. In other words, we can recover the latent heat of evaporation by condensing the water vapor, forming liquid water. Condensing one gram of water vapor at 20°C to form water at the same temperature releases 585 calories. From this we can see the importance of water as a carrier of heat. Evaporation removes heat, supplied by the sun, from the sea surface. This heat is returned, warming the atmosphere, when the vapor condenses to fall as rain or snow. This process of heat transport by water vapor accounts for the mild winters of humid coastal areas. The abundant rainfall releases heat in the atmosphere, preventing the much lower winter temperatures found in the drier interior regions away from the oceans. We will consider the effect of the oceans on the world's climate in greater detail in Chapter 6.

QUESTIONS

1. List the states of matter. Describe the essential features of each.
2. Why does ice fracture rather than flow when you hit it?
3. Draw a diagram showing how two water molecules are linked by a hydrogen bond. How does the presence of this bond cause water to be liquid at room temperatures?
4. Define latent heat. Why is the latent heat of evaporation of water greater than the latent heat of melting?
5. Why does newly formed sea ice have more salt in it than sea ice formed in a previous year?
6. How much heat (in calories) is required to bring 5 grams of ice at 0°C to liquid water at 5°C?
7. How much heat (in calories) must be removed per square centimeter of water surface to cool a column of water 100 m thick by 1°C?
8. How much heat (in calories) would be required to raise the average temperature of the entire ocean (3.5°C) to 20°C?

9. Calculate the amount of heat necessary to evaporate the water (approximately 100 cm) removed from the ocean surface each year. What happens to this heat? (Latent heat of evaporation at 20°C is 585 calories per gram.)

10. Explain why the relative density of two liquids determines which will float above the other?

11. Explain why lakes rarely freeze all the way to the bottom.

12. Why does the temperature of an ice-water or water-water vapor mixture remain fixed until one of the two components disappears?

SUPPLEMENTARY READING

Davis, Kenneth S. and John Arthur Day, *Water: The Mirror of Science*. Garden City, N. Y.: Anchor Books, Doubleday and Company, Inc., 1961.

Chapter 5

Sea Water—A Salt Solution

Sea water is a mixture of salts of nearly constant composition, combined with variable amounts of water. Water, as the major component, determines most of the physical properties of sea water. In this section we consider the composition of the salts and gases dissolved in sea water. In particular we will examine the changes in water properties resulting from the addition of sea salts.

SEA SALTS

It is easy to evaporate the water in sea water, leaving behind the salts, a complex mixture (Fig. 5-1) containing at least traces of most elements. Despite the large number of elements dissolved in sea water, only a few are present in large amounts. Six elements comprise more than 99 per cent of the sea salts (Fig. 5-2).

The oceans are well mixed. As a consequence, the relative abundance of the major components in sea salt is essentially constant, regardless of where in the ocean the sample was taken. Only the water content of the mixture varies, within rather restricted limits. *This near-constancy of composition for the major components provides the oceanographer with an extremely useful method of determining the salt content of sea water.*

Taking advantage of the constant proportions of the major salts in sea water, the oceanographer uses **chlorinity** — the amount of chloride ion present in one kilogram of water — to determine the salt content of sea water. Since chloride ion constitutes 55.0 per cent of the sea salt (Fig. 5-2), we can calculate the total amount of dissolved salts in a kilogram of sea water, the **salinity.** For our purposes, the salinity (S), in parts per thousand (‰), or grams of salt per kilogram of sea water, can be calculated by

$$S(‰) = 1.8Cl(‰)$$

where Cl, the chlorinity, is the amount of chlorine (in grams) per kilogram of sea water.

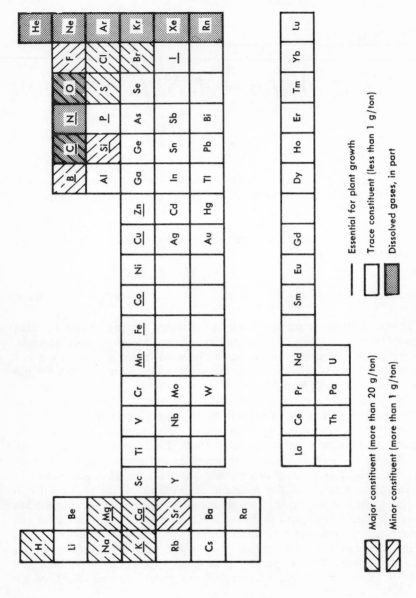

Fig. 5-1. Elements in sea water.

Major constituent (more than 20 g/ton)

Minor constituent (more than 1 g/ton)

Essential for plant growth

Trace constituent (less than 1 g/ton)

Dissolved gases, in part

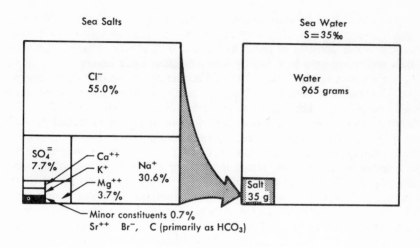

Fig. 5-2. Relative proportions of water and dissolved salts in sea water.

Electrical conductivity — the ability of sea water to transmit an electrical current — is frequently used to determine salinity because of the speed and precision with which the analyses can be done. Increased salinity enhances the electrical conductivity of sea water. Decreased salinity inhibits the electrical conductivity.

To get some idea of the complicated chemistry of sea water, we might try making our own. Using the "recipe" given in Table 5-1, we can make

Table 5-1. Recipe for Artificial Sea Water.

NaCl	23.48 grams	NaHCO$_3$	0.192 grams
MgCl$_2$	4.98	KBr	0.096
Na$_2$SO$_4$	3.92	H$_3$BO$_3$	0.026
CaCl$_2$	1.10	SrCl$_2$	0.024
KCl	0.66	NaF	0.003

add H$_2$O to form 1000 grams of solution

a salt mixture which closely resembles normal sea water. For marine organisms tolerant of a wide range of conditions, our salt water may be an acceptable substitute for sea water. More delicate marine organisms may find it completely unacceptable, dying shortly after being put into it. By comparing the number of elements included in our recipe with those present in normal sea water (Fig. 5-1), we can begin to understand why certain organisms may not be able to tolerate our mixture.

INTERACTIONS BETWEEN WATER AND SEA SALTS

The separation of charges on the water molecule, which enables it to form hydrogen bonds, also acts to give water unusual solvent properties. Because water consists of polar molecules, it is able to dissolve the many solids which are held together by intermolecular **ionic bonds.**

Ionic bonds result from the mutual attraction of two differently charged ions. In crystals of common table salt (sodium chloride) the sodium atom loses one electron, becoming the positively charged sodium ion, Na^+. The chlorine atom gains the electron, forming the negatively charged chloride ion, Cl^-. Elements losing electrons (electron donors) are known as **cations;** those gaining electrons (electron acceptors) are known as **anions.** In the presence of water, the ions retain their charges. But the attraction between ions, which held the crystal together when it was dry, is disrupted by the presence of the water molecules. The charges on the polar water molecules become oriented around each ion, forming a sheath of water molecules which effectively isolates each ion from its neighbors (Fig. 5-3). Consequently, the crystal dissolves. In solution the ions retain their sheath

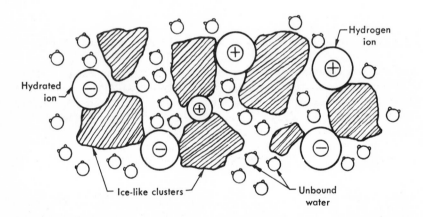

Fig. 5-3. Schematic representation of sea-water structure. (After R. A. Horne, "The Physical Chemistry and Structure of Sea Water," *Water Resources Research,* 1 [1965], 269.)

of water molecules, forming **hydrated ions.** In sea water, as in pure water, we have a structure of ice-like clusters surrounded by unbonded water molecules. The hydrated ions formed from the dissolved salts have some effect on the structure and physical properties of sea water.

SOME PHYSICAL PROPERTIES OF SEA WATER

A physical chemist can measure the effect of sea salt on the water structure by measuring changes in a number of water properties. Changing the salinity of water from 0‰ to 40‰ causes the **viscosity** — resistance of a liquid to flowing — to increase about 5 per cent.

We will consider the effect of sea salts in water on two closely related properties — the **temperature of maximum density** and the **temperature of initial freezing.** As mentioned previously, sea salts do not fit into the crystal structure of ice. In fact, the presence of sea salt inhibits ice formation, as seen in the depression of the initial freezing point (Fig. 5-4).

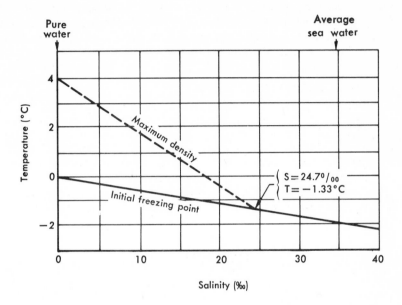

Fig. 5-4. Effect of salinity on the temperature of maximum density and the initial freezing point of sea water.

Adding more sea salt causes the salt mixture to freeze at temperatures below 0°C. For example, sea water with a salinity of 16‰ begins to freeze at −0.86°C, at a salinity of 32‰ it begins to freeze at −1.74°C, and at 40‰, at −2.20°C.

Sea water does not freeze completely at a given temperature as does pure water — in other words, *sea water has no fixed freezing point.* The reason is easily understood. As sea water freezes, the sea salts are excluded from the ice structure. Consequently, the remaining sea water is more saline and freezes at a lower temperature. Unless cooled to very low temperatures, there is always a small amount of highly concentrated brine remaining unfrozen.

The causes of the depression of the initial freezing point also explain the depression of the temperature of maximum density. The sea salts apparently inhibit the development of the ice-like clusters that causes the volume expansion of pure liquid water near the freezing point. Adding sea salt to water causes a progressive lowering of the temperature of max-

imum density. At a salinity of 24.7‰, the temperature of maximum
density and the initial freezing temperature coincide at −1.33°C. At
salinities greater than 24.7‰ sea water does not exhibit a density maximum. Hence normal sea water (salinity of 35‰) becomes progressively
denser as the temperature is lowered until the water begins to freeze.

The changes in certain properties of water, due to the presence of
sea salt, can be measured and used as an indicator of the salinity of the
water. An example is the **refractive index,** an indication of the relative
speed of light rays passing through sea water. Although little used by
oceanographers, the refractive index of sea water can easily be measured
with simple devices, and could provide useful information where the sea
water exhibits large salinity changes.

DISSOLVED GASES IN SEA WATER

In addition to salt, normal sea water contains small amounts of dissolved gases from the atmosphere (Fig. 5-5). Because of the large area
of the sea-air interface and its constant stirring by winds and waves, atmospheric gases usually dissolve in the surface waters. Water of a certain
temperature and salinity is said to be **saturated** with gas when the amount
of gas entering the water balances the amount leaving during the same
period of time. In other words, at saturation, the gas dissolved in the

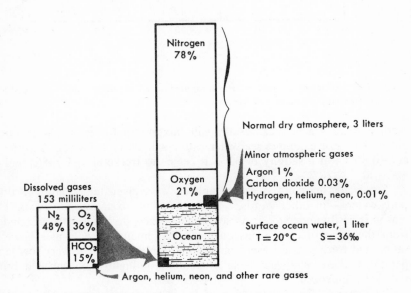

Fig. 5-5. **Gases dissolved in saturated sea water (salinity 36‰, temperature
20°C) in contact with a dry atmosphere.**

water is in equilibrium with the overlying atmosphere. Surface sea water is normally saturated with atmospheric gases.

The amount of gas which can be dissolved in sea water in contact with the atmosphere is determined by the temperature and salinity of the water. Increasing the temperature or salinity reduces the amount of gas dissolved by sea water. Of the two factors, the influence of temperature is the most important. Like water temperature and salinity, the dissolved gas content of a bit of sea water is controlled by conditions existing in the area where that sea water was last at the surface.

Once a particular mass of water sinks beneath the surface, the dissolved gases can no longer exchange with the atmospheric gases. Two things may happen. First, the amount of gas in a bit of water may remain unchanged except by the movement (diffusion) of gas molecules through the water — a slow process — or by mixing with other water masses containing different amounts of dissolved gas. In general, nitrogen and the rare gases, argon (Ar), helium (He), neon (Ne), and krypton (Kr), behave in this manner; we say that their concentrations are **conservative properties.** (Salinity is another example of a conservative property of sea water.) Sea water is nearly saturated at all depths with nitrogen and the rare gases. By studying the slight deviations from the saturation or equilibrium concentrations, physical oceanographers learn about mixing processes and deep-water movements in the ocean.

Dissolved oxygen and carbon dioxide in sea water exhibit a second type of behavior, also interesting to the physical oceanographer. In addition to mixing and diffusion, these gases are involved in biological and inorganic processes changing their concentrations. Hence, their concentrations are examples of **non-conservative properties.** In other words, oxygen and carbon dioxide may be generated or depleted at varying rates in the ocean. Variations in the dissolved oxygen concentration can be used to trace subsurface movements.

The amount of carbon dioxide held by saturated sea water is unusually large. This results from a series of chemical reactions in water involving carbon dioxide. These reactions are shown schematically as follows:

$$CO_2(gas) + H_2O \rightleftharpoons H_2CO_3 \rightleftharpoons H^+ + HCO_3^- \rightleftharpoons 2H^{++} + CO_3^{--}$$

| carbon dioxide | + | liquid water | $\rightleftharpoons$ | carbonic acid | $\rightleftharpoons$ | hydrogen ion | + | bicarbonate | $\rightleftharpoons$ | 2 hydrogen ions | + | carbonate ion |

The double arrows indicate that the chemical reactions are reversible; they may proceed in either direction. Although carbon dioxide enters the ocean as a gas, little remains as dissolved gas molecules (CO_2). Instead, most of the carbon dioxide reacts with the water to form carbonic acid (H_2CO_3). In normal sea water the carbonic acid reacts further, forming mostly bicarbonate ions (HCO_3^-) and lesser amounts of carbonate ions (CO_3^{--}). These reactions play an important role in sea water in maintaining the balance between acids (represented in our equation by hydrogen ions) and bases (represented by carbonate ions and bicarbonate ions).

Dissolved oxygen is less complicated, behaving in sea water more or less like nitrogen. The complications concerning the abundance and distribution of dissolved oxygen arise from the metabolic processes of plants and animals living in the oceans. Free oxygen is formed during **photosynthesis** — the process by which carbon (derived from carbon dioxide) and water are combined by chlorophyll in the presence of sunlight to form carbohydrates such as sugars and starches. Photosynthesis can be represented as follows:

$$6CO_2 + 6H_2O + \text{energy} \quad \underset{\text{(Respiration)}}{\overset{\text{(Photosynthesis)}}{\underset{\text{animals}}{\overset{\text{plants}}{\rightleftharpoons}}}} \quad C_6H_{12}O_6 + 6O_2(\text{gas})$$

carbon   water   animals   carbohydrate   oxygen
dioxide   (Respiration)

In order to obtain energy from their food, animals essentially "burn" the carbohydrates, using oxygen and releasing carbon dioxide and water. This may be considered to be the reverse of photosynthesis. Thus, in the deep sea, the abundance of dissolved oxygen and bicarbonate (or carbonate) tend to be inversely related. As one is used up, the other is released.

Photosynthesis requires energy from sunlight. Hence food and oxygen are produced only in the sunlit near-surface ocean, called the **photic** or **photosynthetic zone.** Tiny floating plants, called **phytoplankton,** are responsible for most of the photosynthesis in the ocean.

The shade-loving phytoplankton are usually most abundant a few meters or tens of meters below the sea surface. There, intense photosynthetic activity frequently releases oxygen which is dissolved but cannot readily escape to the atmosphere through the sea surface. Such near-surface waters are frequently supersaturated with dissolved oxygen; that is, they contain more than the equilibrium amount of oxygen.

While local production of oxygen by plants is common in the surface, sunlit waters, it does not occur at greater depths because there is insufficient sunlight to provide the necessary energy for photosynthesis. Thus the *production of food and oxygen in the ocean is a near-surface phenomenon.*

Although a water parcel may sink below the surface, preventing further photosynthesis by plants, animals continue to eat and metabolize food produced at the surface. Animals use dissolved oxygen from the water which is no longer being replenished by exchange with the atmosphere or by photosynthesis. Consequently, the dissolved oxygen concentration in deep-ocean water decreases and continues to decrease until that bit of water is again at the ocean surface to equilibrate with the oxygen in the atmosphere.

Using the changes in dissolved oxygen concentrations, chemical or physical oceanographers can trace deep-ocean water movements from the surface area where the water mass is formed, until it either reappears at the ocean surface or its distinctive properties are appreciably changed by mixing with other water masses.

DENSITY OF SEA WATER

Density of sea water is controlled by three factors: temperature, salinity, and pressure. Temperature and salinity are the most important. In the open ocean, the density of sea water varies only between relatively narrow limits. Consequently, the oceanographer must determine the density of sea water with great precision and work with slight variations in density.

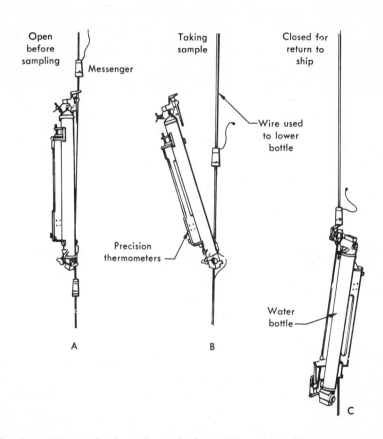

Open
before
sampling

Messenger

Taking
sample

Closed for
return to
ship

Wire used
to lower
bottle

Precision
thermometers

Water
bottle

A

B

C

Fig. 5-6. Nansen bottle and attached special precision thermometers, used for accurate temperature measurements and collecting water samples for salinity determinations. The open bottle is lowered to the desired location. A brass cylinder, called a messenger is released (A) causing the bottle to invert, (B) closing valves at each end and enclosing a water sample. The special precision thermometers record the temperature at that instant. The water and thermometers are then hoisted to the ship (C). (Modified after U. S. Naval Oceanographic Office, *Instruction Manual for Oceanographic Observations,* H. O. Pub. 607, [Washington, D. C.: 1955], p. 9.)

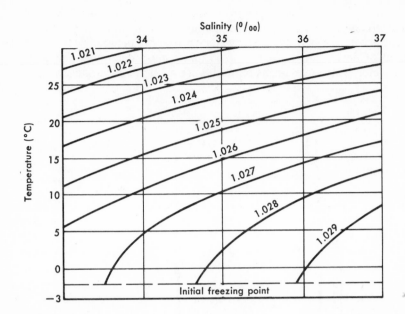

Fig. 5-7. Changes in the density (g/cm³) of sea water caused by changes in salinity and temperature. (Modified after U. S. Naval Oceanographic Office, *Instruction Manual for Oceanographic Observations*, H. O. Pub. 607, [Washington, D. C.: 1955], p. 42.)

Normally, density of sea water is calculated from precise measurements of temperature (accurate to ±0.02°C) and salinity (accurate to ±0.02‰) of water samples (Fig. 5-6). From these measurements, density* is calculated to a precision of one part in 50,000. (This is equivalent to balancing your bank account of $500 to the nearest penny.)

Fig. 5-7 shows the changes in water density for salinities between 33 and 37‰ and temperatures from −3 to 30°C. This encompasses the temperature and salinity range of most sea water samples. We can compare the relative effects of temperature and salinity on sea water density using

---

*Actually, it is the density *difference* that is most important to the oceanographer. To facilitate working with density data, a new quantity σ_t (pronounced sigma-t) is used. It is the density at the surface of a water parcel at its original temperature and salinity. It is computed by:

$$\sigma_t = (\text{density} - 1)\,1000.$$

Thus, if we calculate the density of a sea water sample to be 1.02493, this is equivalent to σ_t −24.93. In effect, we have simplified the expression of density. It is easier to work numerically with the difference between σ_t's of 25.61 and 24.93 than their equivalents of 1.02561 and 1.02493 written as density.

Fig. 5-7. At 30°C, a change of salinity from 34 to 35.3‰ changes the density from 1.021 to 1.022. At 37‰ a comparable change in density is accomplished by cooling the water from 27.5 to 24.3°C.

WATER DENSITY AND STABILITY

Water density is extremely important. The relative density of a particular bit of sea water controls the depth at which that water parcel will occur in the ocean. You will remember that the density of sea water is determined primarily by its temperature and salinity. Density of sea water is increased by increasing the salinity or by cooling the water. Conversely, sea water becomes less dense when it is warmed or the salinity reduced by mixing with fresh water.

It is important to understand the factors controlling sea water density. Also it is important to understand the effects of changing the density of sea water. Changes in density, resulting from processes occurring primarily at the ocean surface, are a primary cause of the sluggish deep-ocean currents.

To understand the significance of water density we can conduct the following experiment. Fill a beaker with fresh water from the tap (Fig.

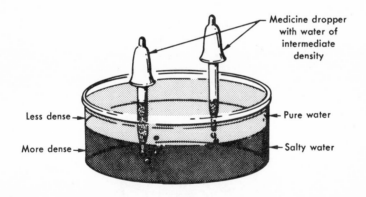

Fig. 5-8. Vertical movements of water of intermediate density in a stable, two-layered, density-stratified system.

5-8). Fill a medicine dropper with salty water, colored with ink or food coloring. If you put a drop of colored salty water into the beaker of fresh water at the same temperature, you will find that it will sink to the bottom because the salty water is denser than the fresh water. Conversely, a drop of colored fresh water put into a beaker of salty water will remain at the surface because it is less dense.

For the next experiment, we can make a two-layered system like the ocean. Dense, salty water can be formed by dissolving as much salt as the water in a half-filled container will hold. (Add salt until some remains undissolved even after vigorous stirring.) Then carefully pour fresh water on top of the salty water. After the water movements caused by adding the fresh water layer have died out, you should have a stable, two-layered system wherein the denser salty water lies below the fresh water. The system is stable because it will remain essentially unchanged unless you add energy. This energy could be added by either stirring or heating the container.

Now if you add a drop of slightly salty colored water, it will sink through the fresh water, coming to rest at an intermediate level. The exact level will depend on the change of density with depth and the density of the colored drop of salty water. We have a **stable density distribution** if the most dense water is at the bottom and the least dense on top. Waters of intermediate density occur at intermediate depths. Stability is essentially the resistance to change in the system. *If we slightly disturb a stable system, it will return to its initial state after the disturbance ceases.*

When the drop of salty water is first added to the system, we have momentarily an **unstable density distribution** because the drop is denser than the surrounding fresh water and sinks spontaneously. Conversely, if we put the eyedropper down into the very salty water and release a drop, it should rise because we have again created an unstable density distribution. The water drop is less dense than the surrounding water and will rise. Thus *an unstable system spontaneously tends to move toward a more stable configuration.*

We can also make a **neutrally stable distribution** if we thoroughly mix the water so that the water density is the same throughout. Also, if our two-layered system is allowed to stand long enough, the salt will diffuse through the water eventually resulting in equal water density throughout. In this case, the system does not return to its initial state after a disturbance. Hence, *a neutrally stable system is easily mixed.*

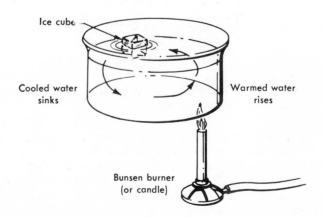

Ice cube

Cooled water
sinks

Warmed water
rises

Bunsen burner
(or candle)

Fig. 5-9. **Convection caused by warming the water at the bottom and cooling it at the top.**

So far we have only considered density changes accompanying salinity changes. But we know that temperature changes also cause changes in water density. This can be shown by heating one side of a beaker's bottom with a candle or Bunson burner (Fig. 5-9). The warmed water is less dense and rises above the heated area. Cooler water sinks on the other side of the beaker and flows along the beaker bottom to replace the rising water. The water movements can be made visible by adding a small amount of ink or food color.

Our experiments show water movements resulting from density changes. Such density-controlled vertical movements of water also occur in the ocean. The process is known as **convection;** the resulting water movements are known as **convection currents.**

Convective movements of air are important in the atmosphere, which, as in our experiment, is warmed at the bottom and cooled at the top. *The oceans, however, are both heated and cooled at the top.* Consequently, convective currents are generally less important in the oceans than in the atmosphere. We can simulate the situation in the oceans by shining an infra-red lamp on the surface of a dish of cool water. This will create a stable system with warm water above cold. Fairly vigorous mixing is required to mix a warm water layer with underlying colder water.

RESOURCES FROM SEA WATER

Water is probably the ocean's most valuable potential resource. Ships at sea have long obtained their drinking water by distilling sea water. As the world population expands, coastal cities in arid regions will doubtlessly derive part or all of their water from the oceans. In short, man is trying to duplicate the natural water cycle, evaporating sea water to recover fresh water. The problem is to recover the fresh water at the location where it is to be used. Technically feasible, desalinization processes need only large amounts of inexpensive energy to make them an economic reality for many water-short regions.

For many centuries, sea water has been an important source of sodium chloride. Evaporating basins, located primarily in the relatively dry coastal regions, employ solar energy to evaporate the water. The chemistry of the brine is closely controlled so that only the sodium chloride or other desirable components of sea salt are recovered at a single stage. Otherwise the salt recovered from sea water must be treated to remove such components as $MgSO_4 \cdot 7H_2O$, a bitter-tasting, laxative substance commonly known as Epsom salt, and $CaCO_3$, calcium carbonate, which makes a gritty impurity in table salt. Evaporating ponds for the extraction of sea salts operate near the southern end of San Francisco Bay. Most of the salts obtained from sea water are used by the chemical industry.

Magnesium (Mg) is another important material extracted commercially from sea water; it is used in the chemical industry and as a lightweight metal. Bromine (Br), extracted from sea water, is a component of anti-knock compounds in motor fuels.

Men have long been intrigued by the huge amounts of gold present in the ocean. The concentration of gold in sea water is extremely low, 4 grams of gold per million tons of sea water. Because of the immense volume of the oceans, this amounts to approximately 5 million tons, or $25,000 for each of the 200 million people in the United States. One reason that no one is enjoying this wealth is that the cost of recovering the gold is many times greater than its value. The extremely low concentrations of many other valuable materials also prevent — at least for the present — their commercial extraction from sea water.

QUESTIONS

1. List three substances commercially extracted from sea water. Give some uses for each. What other substances do you think might be valuable?
2. Define salinity and chlorinity. List three techniques by which salinity may be determined.
3. Why does table salt (NaCl) dissolve when put in water?
4. How does the temperature of maximum density for fresh water compare with the temperature of maximum density in normal sea water ($S = 35‰$)?
5. Why does sea water not freeze completely at a fixed temperature?
6. Water with a salinity of 10‰ begins to freeze at what temperature? At what temperature is it most dense?
7. Why are dissolved oxygen concentrations in sea water said to be non-conservative properties?
8. Which elements in sea water are essential for plant growth? If these are depleted in the near-surface layers, what effect would this have on the local production of food in the sea?
9. List the factors controlling the density of sea water. Explain the effect of each.

SUPPLEMENTARY READING

Harvey, H. W., *The Chemistry and Fertility of Sea Waters.* Cambridge, England: At the University Press, 1960. General reference, technical, good bibliography.
Woodcock, A. H., "Salt and Rain," *Scientific American,* October, 1957.

Chapter 6

The Open Ocean

Light, temperature, and salinity are the most important variable factors in the marine environment. Their distribution results from the absorption of the incoming solar radiation (**insolation**) in the surface ocean and the resulting transport of heat and water vapor over the earth's surface. Part of this energy from the sun heats the ocean, which in turn supplies energy to drive the atmospheric circulation. Much of the incoming solar energy is used at the ocean surface to evaporate water.

The atmosphere and surface ocean are parts of a vast, inefficient sun-powered engine which changes only a very small fraction of the incoming solar energy into winds or water movements. To simplify our discussion of the oceans we will first investigate the distribution of light, heat, and salinity in the open ocean, essentially ignoring any water movements. In following chapters we consider wind-driven surface-ocean currents, the density-controlled deep-ocean circulation, and the ocean circulation near the continents.

LAYERED STRUCTURE OF THE OCEAN

Absorption of the incoming solar radiation in the surface ocean causes a layered structure of the open ocean consisting of three zones: the **surface, pycnocline,** and **deep zones** (Fig. 6-1). The **surface zone** undergoes major changes as a result of seasonal variations in heating, cooling, evaporation, and precipitation. In the polar and subpolar oceans, freezing of surface sea water to form **sea ice** is an important process. These processes control the temperature, salinity, and therefore the density of the surface waters.

The surface zone contains the least dense water, usually as a result of higher temperatures caused by warming of the surface waters by the sun. The thickness of the surface zone is controlled by the depth of surface mixing, caused primarily by the winds. In certain areas, vertical water movements (convective movements) are caused by density changes resulting from changes in temperature and salinity. Mixing of the water in the surface zone results in its near-neutral stability. Water particles can move

65

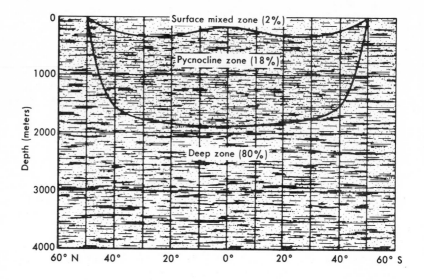

Fig. 6-1.   Schematic diagram of the ocean's layered structure and the relative volume of the ocean (in per cent) contained in each zone. Note that the deep zone comes to the surface near the poles in the Northern and Southern Hemispheres.

vertically rather easily within the mixed zone. In general, water in the surface zone has ample opportunity to adjust to local climatic conditions and to equilibrate with the atmosphere.

Below the surface zone is the **pycnocline zone,** where water density changes greatly with depth. Because of these large changes in density with depth, the water of the pycnocline zone exhibits great stability. Hence the pycnocline acts as an effective though slightly leaky barrier to vertical water movements. *The pycnocline acts as the floor to the surface circulation and to seasonal changes in temperature and salinity of the ocean water.*

In addition, *the pycnocline zone is the ceiling for the deep zone and its circulation.* The pycnocline prevents the deep ocean waters from readily mixing with the surface waters or equilibrating with the atmosphere except in the high latitudes (Fig. 6-1). In the polar ocean, the pycnocline is usually absent and the deep ocean waters are exposed to the surface climatic conditions. In these regions, the deep-ocean waters exchange gases with the atmosphere, giving up their excess carbon dioxide and replacing their dissolved oxygen. Exchange of gases in these regions is greatly facilitated by the extensive mixing resulting from the strong winds and frequent storms typical of these latitudes.

LIGHT IN THE OCEAN

At the sea surface, much of the solar energy is in the visible part of the electromagnetic spectrum. We experience this part of the solar spectrum as light. We experience the infra-red part of the spectrum as heat. When careless at the beach, we may experience the ultra-violet part of the spectrum as a sunburn.

Infra-red radiation is quickly absorbed in passing through water; it is virtually absent at depths greater than one meter (Fig. 6-2). The visible

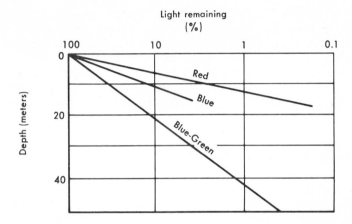

Fig. 6-2. Amount of different colors of light remaining at various depths in the ocean. (Note that the scale of light remaining changes by factors of ten.)

part of the spectrum is also absorbed by the water and changed to heat. Absorption of the insolation is responsible for warming the ocean at its surface.

Plants require light for photosynthesis. Photosynthetic production by plants in the ocean is thus limited to the **photic zone.** The amount of insolation used by plants in photosynthesis is relatively small (about 0.1 per cent of the insolation). This is, however, the energy source for all food production in the ocean, and all marine animals depend on it, whether they live at the ocean surface or on its floor.

Even in particle-free sea water, light penetrates only the surface zone; nearly all the visible light has been absorbed at 100 m depth (Fig. 6-2). In parts of the subtropical ocean, sea water is relatively free of particles and dissolved organic substances. At 200 m in clear ocean water, less than 0.01 per cent of the incoming radiation remains as visible light. Light at these depths is usually blue-green in color.

A striking feature of many parts of the open ocean is the blue, almost luminous color of the water. The blue color indicates that surface waters of such regions are devoid of particles. These are the "deserts" of the ocean whose nutrient-poor surface waters cannot support the growth of abundant phytoplankton.

The color of these waters is a consequence of scattering and absorption of light. Bluish colors are more readily scattered by water than are the reddish colors. In addition, water is more transparent (absorbs less) to the blue colors than to the reds. Hence the combination of scattering and absorption results in the observed blue color of particle-free sea water.

An abundance of particles in the water changes its scattering properties, frequently giving the water a more greenish color. In addition, colored particles or dissolved materials may themselves give the sea water a variety of hues. Sea water may exhibit a brownish, greenish, or even reddish* color depending on the nature of the particles or organisms in the water.

Suspended and dissolved materials also limit the depth of light penetration. In turbid sea water at 10 m depth, the light levels may be comparable to those at 100 m in nonturbid sea water, and the light remaining is more yellow green.

TEMPERATURE — HEATING AND COOLING

The ocean is an efficient absorber of incoming solar energy. Heating of the ocean surface occurs only during the daylight hours, and surface

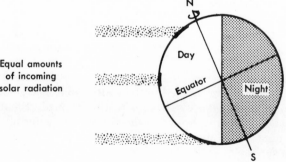

Fig. 6-3. **Variations in the incoming solar radiation per unit area resulting from variations in the angle at which the sun's rays strike the earth's surface. Conditions are shown for northern summer.**

---

*"Red tides," sometimes observed in coastal or nearshore water, are caused by the prolific growth of certain red-colored marine organisms.

waters are warmest in late afternoon. The amount of energy absorbed by
the ocean depends on local cloud cover and the altitude of the sun. The
sun's altitude at a given location depends in turn on latitude and the time
of the year (Fig. 6-3). More solar energy is absorbed when the sun is high
in the sky during local summer. Much less solar energy is absorbed when
the sun is near the horizon in local winter. The sun is well above the
horizon at all seasons in the tropics and subtropics. Near the poles, the
sun is never far above the horizon. Consequently, polar and subpolar regions receive much less insolation than the tropics and subtropics. In
general, *the earth is heated in the tropics and subtropics. It is cooled by
radiating energy, primarily from the polar and subpolar regions* (Fig. 6-4).

The energy received from the sun at the top of the earth's atmosphere
is thought to be relatively constant, averaging about 0.5 calories per square
centimeter of earth's surface per minute. After passing through the atmos-

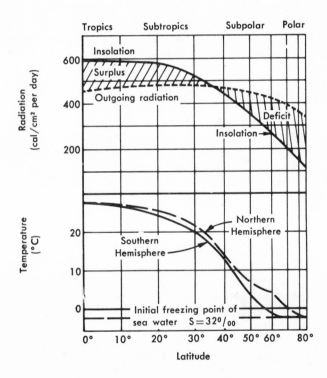

Fig. 6-4. **Radiation balance in the Northern Hemisphere and average surface
ocean temperatures in the Northern and Southern Hemispheres. (Heat budget
after H. G. Houghton, "On the Annual Heat Balance of the Northern Hemisphere,"** *Journal of Meteorology,* **11 [1954], p. 7; Ocean surface temperature
data from W. E. Forsythe, editor,** *Smithsonian Physical Tables,* **9th rev. ed.
[Washington, D. C.: Smithsonian Institution, 1964], p. 726.)**

phere, the average insolation at the earth's surface is 0.25 calories per
square centimeter per minute on a 24-hour basis.

If the average surface insolation were confined to the upper 1 m of
the surface zone, ocean surface temperatures would increase about 3.5°C
in one day. However, the observed mean daily temperature variation in the
open ocean is only 0.2-0.3°C. This indicates that the daily input of solar
energy is quickly mixed through the near-surface waters to depths of 10
m or more. Consequently, the heat gained by the ocean during the day is
distributed through a fairly thick surface zone, and is not readily lost at
night. This mixing, in addition to water's relatively high heat capacity,
prevents a large daily change in surface water temperature. On land, the
sun's energy is retained at the surface of a sun-warmed rock during the
day, and is therefore readily lost at night. Consequently, the daily temperature range of the land is much greater than that of the ocean.

If the ocean retained all the solar heat it absorbed, ocean water temperatures would reach the boiling point in slightly less than 300 years. Obviously, this is not happening now. Remains of certain ancient marine
organisms preserved in rocks suggest that the ocean surface temperatures
have changed little in the past one or two billion years of the ocean's
existence. This indicates that each year the oceans lose as much energy
as they absorb from insolation (Table 6-1).

Table 6-1. Heat Balance at the Ocean Surface.

	Heating	Cooling
	(calories/cm² per minute)	
Incoming solar radiation	0.25	
(24-hour average)		
Back radiation to space		0.10
Evaporation		0.13
Atmospheric warming by conduction		0.02
TOTAL	0.25	0.25

Three major processes are involved in this loss of heat from the ocean
surface: (1) radiation of heat back into space, (2) heating the atmosphere,
and (3) evaporation of water from the sea surface. Each process involves
the loss of heat from the sea surface. *Thus the sea is not only warmed at
its surface, but cooled there as well.*

Heat loss from the ocean surface continues day and night and in all
seasons. The surface of the oceans is warm and radiates energy, just as
does the sun's surface. About 40 per cent of the insolation received by
the oceans is lost by back radiation to outer space (Fig. 6-4). Most of
the ocean's radiation back to space is in the infra-red part of the spectrum
instead of the visible spectrum emitted by the much hotter surface of
the sun.

A small fraction of the ocean's heat loss goes directly into warming the
atmosphere. The heat is transferred to the atmosphere by conduction just

as a pan set on a hot stove obtains its heat. Usually, ocean surface waters are about 1°C warmer than the overlying atmosphere.

About half of the ocean's heat loss is due to evaporation of water from the surface. The heat transferred is often referred to as **latent heat.** It is the heat required to change liquid water to water vapor. This heat is given off to the atmosphere when the water vapor condenses to fall as rain or snow. The atmosphere gains much of its heat through this process.

One effect of heating the ocean's surface is to cause the ocean's layered structure, which we discussed previously. The rapid vertical transfer of heat in the surface zone creates a nearly **isothermal (iso**—equal, **thermal**—temperature) mixed surface zone. The heat is not transported deep enough to warm the cold bottom waters. There, temperatures do not change with the seasons, but remain nearly constant at 3.5°C (see Fig. 6-9).

Separating the sun-warmed surface zone and the cold, deep zone is the **thermocline (thermo**—heat, **cline**—slope), where temperature changes greatly with depth (Fig. 6-5). In most of the ocean waters, temperatures decrease slowly with increasing depth below the thermocline.

Changes in temperature cause density changes, so that in most of the world ocean the thermocline basically controls the **pycnocline (pycno**—density, **cline**—slope), and water density increases with increasing depth below the pycnocline.

Unequal distribution of heat on the earth causes large differences in surface water temperatures between the tropics and the poles (Fig. 6-6).

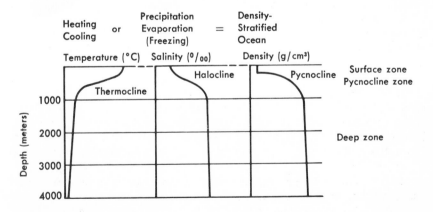

Fig. 6-5. **Basic types of vertical distributions of temperature, salinity, and density in the ocean. (Modified after J. P. Tully, "Oceanographic Regions and Assessment of Temperature Structure in the Seasonal Zone of the North Pacific Ocean,"** *Journal of the Fisheries Research Board, Canada,* **21 [1964], p. 942.)**

72

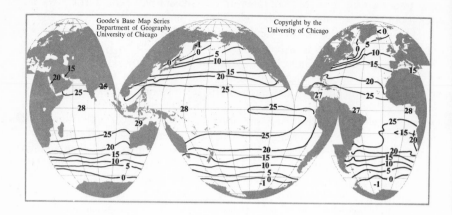

Fig. 6-6. Ocean surface temperatures (°C) in winter, Northern Hemisphere. (Modified after H. J. McLellan, *Elements of Physical Oceanography.* [Oxford: Pergamon Press, 1965], p. 44.)

The surface oceans are warmest (25-30°C) in the tropical and subtropical regions and coldest (down to − 1.7°C) near the poles (Fig. 6-4). In general, belts of equal temperature trend east-west. We shall see that such east-west trends of distributions are common in the open ocean; this is primarily a consequence of the earth's rotation.

Surface **isotherms** — lines connecting points of equal temperature — deviate from the east-west near the continents, especially in the western North Atlantic and western North Pacific Oceans. These deviations are a consequence of continental climatic conditions and currents—some of them quite strong—which tend to flow parallel to the ocean boundaries. Some of these boundary currents transport warm water poleward; others transport cool water toward the equator.

Comparison of the surface water temperatures (Fig. 6-4) for the ocean in the Northern and Southern Hemispheres shows that the oceans of both hemispheres exhibit nearly the same temperature changes with latitude. However several interesting differences are apparent. In the Northern Hemisphere the ocean surface is somewhat warmer than in the Southern Hemisphere. This has been explained as a consequence of the greater abundance of land in the Northern Hemisphere. Note that the differences in surface temperature are greatest in the subpolar oceans, around 60°North and South latitudes. This is the land-dominated belt of the Northern Hemisphere, and the ocean-dominated belt of the Southern Hemisphere (Fig. 1-3).

Also notice that the lowest surface water temperatures in both hemispheres (− 1.7°C) coincide with the temperature of initial freezing (Fig. 5-4) for sea water with a salinity of about 32‰. The freezing or melting of sea ice in the polar oceans acts as a thermostat, essentially fixing surface water temperature. Local surface water temperature cannot go any higher until all the sea ice is melted. Conversely, as long as some surface waters remain unfrozen (at the same salinity) the water temperatures cannot go any lower.

SALINITY — EVAPORATION AND PRECIPITATION

Changes in the salinity of ocean waters are caused primarily by evaporation (removal of fresh water as water vapor), by precipitation (adding fresh water as rain or snow), and by river discharge from the continents. Near the poles, formation of sea ice plays an important role, because nearly fresh water is incorporated in the ice, leaving behind the salts (see Chapter 5). These processes act on the ocean surface, as do the heating and cooling processes (Fig. 6-7). Large changes of salinity with depth (Fig. 6-5) form the **halocline** (**halo** — salt, **cline** — slope).

Salinity changes have a pronounced effect on sea water density (Fig. 5-6). A change in salinity of 1‰ causes a greater density change than does a temperature change of 1°C. Hence in those parts of the ocean where the surface waters (Fig. 6-7) are greatly diluted by excess precipitation (Fig. 6-8), the main pycnocline frequently coincides with the halocline.

Despite the important local effects of reduced surface salinity, over most of the ocean the pycnocline is controlled by the development of the thermocline. This is primarily a result of the relatively large temperature range ($-1.7°$ to $30°C$) of sea water (Fig. 6-9). In contrast, the range of salinity for most of the ocean is relatively small (33 to 37‰).

The water evaporated from the ocean surface each year is equivalent to a layer about one meter thick. Approximately 90 per cent of this water is returned to the ocean surface as rain. The remainder falls as rain (or snow) on the continents. Eventually this water also returns to the coastal

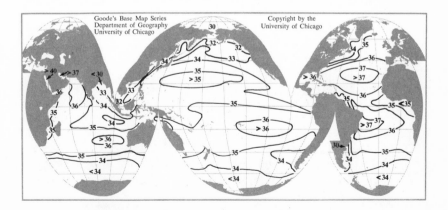

Fig. 6-7. Ocean-surface salinity (‰). (After H. U. Sverdrup, M. W. Johnson, and R. H. Fleming, *The Oceans: Their Physics, Chemistry, and General Biology.* [Englewood Cliffs, N. J.: Prentice-Hall, Inc., 1942], Chart VI.)

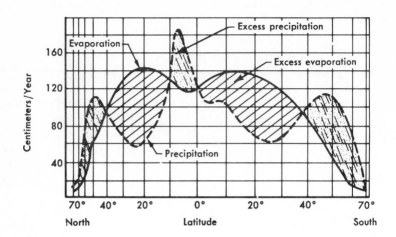

Fig. 6-8. Distribution of evaporation and precipitation over the ocean. (Data from G. Wüst, W. Brogmus, and E. Noodt, "Die zonale Verteilung von Salzgehalt, Niederschlag, Verdunstung, Temperatur und Dichte an der Oberfläche der Ozeane," *Kieler Meeresforschungen,* Band V [1954], p. 146.)

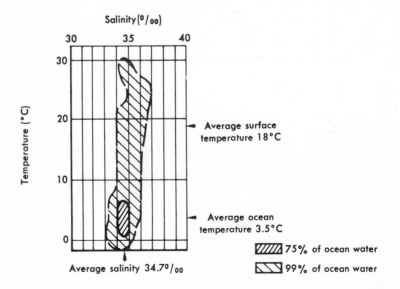

Fig. 6-9. Range of temperature and salinity in the world ocean. (After R. B. Montgomery, "Water Characteristics of Atlantic Ocean and of World Ocean," *Deep-Sea Research,* 5 [1958], p. 144.)

oceans, carried by rivers. We will return to the subject of river discharge in Chapter 9.

If the evaporation and precipitation were equally distributed over the oceans, we would expect a very simple salinity distribution in the surface layers. The available data (Fig. 6-7) on the salinity distribution in surface waters indicate that evaporation and precipitation are not evenly distributed over the ocean surface. Relatively high surface salinities (greater than 35‰) near 30°N and 30°S indicate that these are areas of excess evaporation (Fig. 6-8). Removal of water as water vapor, leaving behind the salt, increases the salinity of these surface waters. The relatively low salinities (less than 35‰) of surface waters in high latitudes indicates that these are areas of excess precipitation. River discharge in these latitudes further reduces the surface salinity. We must bear in mind, however, that *salinity of water in the open ocean varies much less than does the temperature* (Fig. 6-9).

The amount of evaporation from any part of the ocean surface is controlled by (1) the amount of local insolation, (2) the wind speed, and (3) relative humidity of the overlying air. Because of the abundant insolation, the tropics and subtropics (Fig. 6-4) experience large amounts of evaporation (Fig. 6-8). Conversely, there is less evaporation near the poles, where less insolation is available.

Effect of winds on evaporation can also be detected. Maximum amounts of evaporation occur in subtropical regions (around 30°N and 30°S) where the highly persistent Trade Winds blow throughout the year. Also the subtropics are areas of clear skies (high insolation) and relatively dry air. The somewhat reduced evaporation in equatorial regions (Fig. 6-8) is due in part to the light and variable winds which give the region its name, the Doldrums. Regional cloudiness also contributes by diminishing the insolation.

Precipitation is controlled by atmospheric processes* and is beyond the scope of our view of the oceans. It is sufficient for our purposes to note that precipitation is most abundant near the equator and in high latitudes (Fig. 6-8). In these areas of excess precipitation, the salinity of the surface waters is measurably diminished (Fig. 6-7).

CLIMATIC REGIONS OF THE OCEANS

We can distinguish climatic regions in the ocean (Fig. 6-10). These climatic regions are characterized by similarity of the mean conditions at the ocean surface and the dominant processes acting in each region. The simplest classification would separate the surface ocean into **coastal** (or nearshore) **ocean** and the **open ocean.**

The coastal region, discussed in Chapter 9, is the most difficult to characterize. Here the ocean is influenced by the presence of the continents

---

*See A. Miller, *Meteorology*. (Columbus, Ohio: Charles A. Merrill Books, Inc., 1966) for a discussion of the processes controlling precipitation.

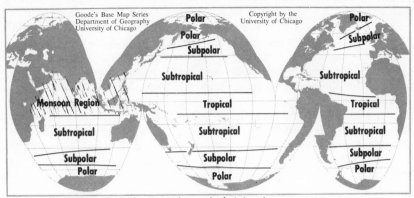

Monsoon region, seasonal reversals of winds and current directions.

Fig. 6-10. **Climatic regions of the open ocean.**

and relatively shallow ocean floor. Away from the continental boundaries, the surface waters show greater uniformity of temperature and salinity. Here it is possible to distinguish climatic zones extending nearly east-west across the ocean (Fig. 6-10, Table 6-2).

Table 6-2.   Open-ocean Climatic Regions in the Surface Zone.

Oceanic Region	Surface heating and cooling cycle or	Net Precipitation (+) Evaporation (−)	Mixing processes	Seasonal temperature range (°C)
Polar	Seasonal melting & freezing of sea ice. Net heat loss.	+	Wind and convective mixing.	Intermediate (5-9)
Subpolar (West Wind Drift)	Seasonal heating and cooling. Net heat loss.	+	Wind and convective mixing.	Intermediate (2-8)
Subtropical	Seasonal heating and cooling. Net heat gain.	−	Wind and convective mixing.	Large (6-18)
Tropical	No seasons Daily heating and cooling. Net heat gain.	+	Wind	Small (<2)

The locations of the boundaries separating the climatic zones are somewhat arbitrary. Except for the limits of the tropics, the boundaries separating climatic regions are commonly marked by **convergences***, where the surface waters tend to flow toward an area and sink. These convergences in the ocean surface correspond somewhat to weather fronts in the atmosphere. They differ in that their position apparently changes little with the seasons.

The **tropical ocean** more or less straddles the equator in the Atlantic and Pacific Oceans, but is displaced to the south of the equator in the Indian Ocean by the well developed monsoons of that region (Fig. 6-10). In the tropics, seasonal changes in temperature are slight and there is generally a large excess of precipitation over evaporation. The weak and variable winds cause little mixing of the surface waters.

On either side of the tropical ocean are the **subtropical oceans,** centered around 30°N and 30°S latitude. The highly persistent Trade Winds continually blow across these parts of the ocean. Because of the prevailing winds and abundant sunshine, evaporation greatly exceeds precipitation in these regions. The subtropical oceans are the major source of water vapor to the atmosphere. On land, the deserts of North America, Africa, and Asia lie within the subtropical zone.

Seasonal temperature changes are relatively large in the subtropical regions, ranging between 6 and 18°C in the surface waters. These temperature changes are greatest near the coast and especially large in the marginal seas, such as the Black Sea. Because of evaporation, the subtropical surface waters have relatively high salinities and tend to be rather warm. When high salinity surface waters cool during the winter, their increased density causes convective mixing in the surface zone. This supplements the wind mixing and is one reason why the regional thermocline lies so deep under the subtropical oceans.

The **subpolar oceans** have an excess of precipitation and lie in a belt of strong winds, especially well developed in the Southern Hemisphere. During the seasons of high rainfall or large river discharge, a well developed halocline may form. During the local summer, a thermocline may also develop.

In coastal regions, runoff from the continents may contribute large amounts of fresh water, measurably reducing local surface salinities. This is especially noticeable in the subpolar part of the North Pacific Ocean, where surface salinities are less than 32‰ along the coast.

The **polar oceans** are profoundly influenced by the seasonal freezing and thawing of sea ice. Some convective mixing in the surface zone almost always accompanies the formation of sea ice. When sea ice begins to freeze, it releases cold, highly saline brine, which mixes with local waters. Near Antarctica, local intensive cooling of relatively high salinity Atlantic waters

---

*Currents can also flow away from an area, known as a **divergence.** Major divergences occur along the equator and near Antarctica. In general, divergences do not separate oceanic climatic zones.

increases their density substantially. Mixing of these chilled surface waters with cold, highly saline brines formed by local formation of sea ice forms the Antarctic Bottom Water. Such cold waters are denser than any other water masses in the ocean. Consequently, this water sinks to the ocean bottom and is found at great depths in all the oceans. The sinking of cold, dense waters in the high latitudes is also thought to prevent the development of a thermocline near the poles.

In the Arctic Sea the surface waters are less saline (Fig. 6-7). When the warming season begins in the spring, the sea ice melts, releasing nearly fresh water at the sea surface. This low salinity water is warmed by the sun and remains near the surface. In autumn, this less saline water loses its heat, but its low density (resulting from its low salinity) prevents it from sinking below the surface. Remaining at the surface, it again freezes during the winter.

Only where waters of relatively high salinity are intensely cooled (usually in the high latitudes) are very dense water masses formed. Where formed, such water masses are effective in increasing the depth of the pycnocline by convective mixing, resulting from the sinking of the denser water from the surface. These subsurface water masses may flow along the ocean bottom if they are dense enough. If not the densest, the water will flow at a level appropriate to its density between the denser bottom waters and the less dense waters of the surface zone. The movement of a water mass of intermediate density, flowing between waters of greater density below and lesser density above, might be compared to inserting a card into a deck of cards.

To recapitulate, *nearly all the processes affecting the properties of sea water act on the ocean surface. Hence, most properties of any water mass, regardless of its present location, were determined when it was last at the ocean surface.* The properties a water mass acquires at the surface depend on the oceanic climate at that spot. The bottom waters formed in the Antarctic region are very cold. Warm, saline water masses form in the Red Sea or Mediterranean Sea. From the observed water properties and their distribution, oceanographers attempt to discover the areas from which the various subsurface waters are derived.

LAND CLIMATES AND THE OCEANS

If the earth were uniformly covered by land or by ocean, the **climate** (average weather) of any point would be determined by its latitude. As we know, the earth's surface is covered by a complex mosaic of water and land. Furthermore, the mountain ranges complicate the distribution of the climatic zones on land. Hence, climate is not determined solely by latitude.

Surface temperatures in the ocean change relatively little, because of water's large heat capacity and the storage of heat throughout the surface zone. The ocean's effect on the land climate is greatest where the prevailing winds blow from the ocean onto the land. Then the coastal areas have a **marine climate**; Seattle and San Francisco are two examples. Marine climates tend to be temperate, and have small seasonal temperature changes.

In contrast, the land is strongly heated during the summer and easily cooled during winter. Where the prevailing winds have blown far across land, a **continental climate** results, characterized by hot summers and cold winters. Most of the Atlantic coast of the United States would fall into this category. The importance of the prevailing wind direction can be seen by comparing the climates of San Francisco and Washington, D. C. Both lie near the ocean at nearly the same latitude, but in Washington the mean annual temperature is about 11° warmer than in San Francisco.

Mountain ranges have major effects on the distribution of climate. The north-south trending mountain ranges of North and South America restrict the ocean's climatic effects to a relatively narrow strip along the coast. In northern Europe, the nearly east-west trending mountains do not restrict the flow of air from the ocean. Thus, much of Europe has a marine climate, influenced by the prevailing winds off the North Atlantic Ocean.

The oceans and land masses also interact on a large scale in the **monsoons,** especially well developed near Asia (Fig. 6-10). The regional winds there are primarily controlled by the seasonal heating and cooling of the Asian continent. During local summer, the land and the air above it is warmed more than the ocean. The warmed air, being less dense, rises over Asia and is replaced by winds blowing from the ocean. These are the southwest monsoons in India, which bring the heavy rains.

During local winter, the opposite condition prevails. The air over the land cools more than the air over the ocean. Becoming denser, the cold air flows from the continent over the adjacent ocean. In India this is the northeast monsoon, the dry season. These large scale changes in the local winds completely change the wind-driven currents in the Northern Indian Ocean. Although monsoons are best developed near the Asian continent, similar effects occur on a smaller scale in other coastal regions, with more localized effects on the currents. For example, the summer rains of the south-central United States are the result of a monsoon-type air circulation bringing moist air from the Gulf of Mexico over the continent.

Comparable effects occur daily during the summer near large bodies of water. The landward flow of air from the ocean during the day creates the **sea breeze.** At night when the land cools, air flows seaward.

QUESTIONS

1. What processes cause seasonal variations in surface water properties? Which are most important in the subtropical ocean? In the polar ocean?

2. What three processes cause heat loss from the ocean's surface? Which of these processes has the greatest effect on the atmosphere? Why?

3. What are the limits of variation in salinity for 75 per cent of ocean water? For 99 per cent of ocean water? What are the corresponding limits for temperature?

4. Why is the variation in water temperature greater than the variations in salinity?

5. In the subtropical oceans a strong thermocline develops above the main thermocline in the summer. What causes it? Why does it gradually deepen during the winter, finally merging with the main regional thermocline?

6. Draw a graph showing the changes in water temperature with depth for (1) an isothermal water column, and (2) a thermocline at 100 m.

7. Draw a graph showing salinity changes with depth for a halocline at 150 m.

8. What effect does the greater abundance of land in the Northern Hemisphere have on the oceans? What effect does the lesser abundance of land in the Southern Hemisphere have on the oceans?

9. List some of the ways in which the oceans affect world climate. How do the oceans affect your local climate?

10. Determine the density of the following water masses, using Fig. 5-7. Which are bottom waters? Which are surface waters? Where did the masses form?

	T ($°C$)	S (‰)	Density (g/cm^3)
Water mass 1	−2	34.7	
Water mass 2	17	35.7	
Water mass 3	4	34.0	
Water mass 4	15	35.0	
Water mass 5	11	34.0	

SUPPLEMENTARY READING

Gordienko, P. A., "The Arctic Ocean," *Scientific American,* May, 1961.

Kort, V. G., "The Antarctic Ocean," *Scientific American,* September, 1962.

Ryther, J. H., "The Sargasso Sea," *Scientific American,* January, 1956.

Stommel, H., "The Anatomy of the Atlantic," *Scientific American,* January, 1955.

_____, "The Circulation of the Abyss," *Scientific American,* July, 1958.

Chapter 7

Ocean Currents

Ocean waters move unceasingly. Anyone who sails or swims in the ocean quickly becomes acquainted with the horizontal water movements we call currents. Some currents are transient features and affect only a small area, such as a beach. These are the ocean's response to local, often seasonal conditions. Other currents are essentially permanent and involve large parts of the world ocean. These currents are the result of the response of the ocean and atmosphere to the flow of energy from the tropics and subtropics to the subpolar and polar regions. In this chapter we are concerned with the large, nearly permanent ocean currents — where they are and how they form.

SURFACE CURRENTS

Our knowledge of the major surface currents is based principally on the compilation of mariners' observations, begun in the 1840's by the pioneer American oceanographer Matthew Fontaine Maury. Ships' courses are deflected by surface currents, causing a discrepancy between the ship's intended and its actual positions after steaming for a period. The local current can be deduced from the direction and apparent speed of the deflected ship's course. Combining thousands of such observations, Maury synthesized a generalized picture of the ocean currents. By using similar data, gathered over many years, we now have a fairly detailed picture of the average ocean surface currents (Fig. 7-1).

Changeable currents, such as the seasonal **Monsoon Currents** near Asia (Fig. 6-10), are not well defined by observations gathered in various seasons over many years. Study of such changeable currents requires that the observations be gathered in a single season. Such nearly instantaneous pictures of ocean conditions are necessary to show the changes resulting from local variations in wind, river runoff, or the influence of the tides.

The circulation of the lower atmosphere and the ocean above the pycnocline are inescapably linked together. We can verify this by comparing a generalized picture of the average planetary winds to the ocean currents (Fig. 7-2). The correspondence is very close, except near Antarctica.

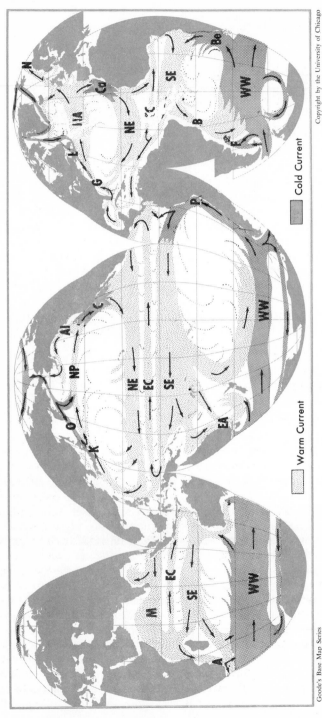

Cold Current

Warm Current

Fig. 7-1. **Ocean-surface currents, January-February. (After "Pilot Charts"** [Washington, D. C.: U. S. Naval Oceanographic Office] various printings and Encyclopedia Britannica World Atlas [Chicago, Illinois: 1955].)

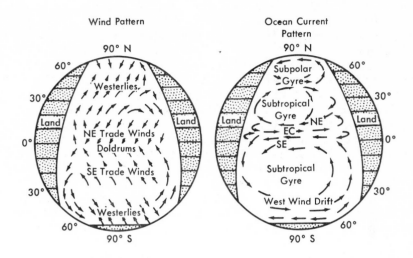

Wind Pattern

Ocean Current Pattern

NE North Equatorial Current

EC Equatorial Counter Current

SE South Equatorial Current

Fig. 7-2. Generalized atmospheric and oceanic circulation. (Modified after R. H. Fleming, "General Features of the Ocean," *Geological Society of America Memoir* 67 [1], [1957], p. 95.)

The ocean current systems correspond rather closely to the generalized wind patterns. The basic pattern of ocean currents is a nearly closed system called a **gyre**. Each ocean has a large current gyre nearly centered in the subtropical regions (approximately 30°N and 30°S) of each hemisphere. In the North Atlantic and Pacific Oceans, smaller current gyres occur in the subpolar ocean, centered at approximately 50°N. In the Southern Hemisphere the West Wind Drift around Antarctica connects the current systems in each of the three oceans.

Each gyre consists of four currents. The northern and southern limits of the gyre are marked by nearly east-west currents, one flowing almost due east, another flowing almost due west. These open ocean currents are joined by boundary currents which flow nearly parallel to the continental margins.

The open ocean currents, such as the **North Pacific Current** or the **North** and **South Equatorial Currents,** flow between three and six kilometers per day, and usually extend 100 to 200 m below the ocean surface. The waters moved by these open-ocean currents remain in the same climatic zone for many months while crossing the ocean. This affords ample opportunity for the surface waters to adjust to the prevailing climatic conditions.

The major eastward-flowing current in the ocean is the **West Wind Drift.** It circles Antarctica and forms part of the Southern Hemisphere current gyres in each of the oceans. In fact, the West Wind Drift may really be several currents, separated by leaky barriers. The narrow opening (Drake Passage) between Cape Horn — the tip of South America — and Antarctica is at least a partial barrier to the passage of this current. Part of the deflected water may join the northward flowing **Peru Current.** There is little doubt that the apparent continuity and simplicity of the West Wind Drift is due to the near absence of land barriers at that latitude. Elsewhere in the ocean the east-west currents are deflected by the continents.

The **western boundary currents** flow generally northward in the Northern Hemisphere, southward in the Southern Hemisphere. They tend to be very powerful currents, especially in the Northern Hemisphere. The relatively narrow, jet-like currents of the **Gulf Stream system** and the **Kuroshio Current** are the most rapid in the ocean, with water moving between 40 and 120 km per day. Also their flow extends the deepest below the surface, extending to depths of 1,000 m or more.

Because of their rapid flow, the surface waters in the western boundary currents do not adjust completely to local climatic conditions. Hence they contribute to the global transfer of heat from the tropics to the poles. The western boundary currents of the Southern Hemisphere, such as the **Brazil Current** and **East Australia Current,** are not as prominent as those in the Northern Hemisphere. In part, this may be due to the scarcity of large continental barriers in the Southern Hemisphere.

The **eastern boundary currents,** such as the **California** or **Canary currents,** are distinctly weaker and broader than their western counterparts (Fig. 7-1). The generally north-south flow of the eastern boundary currents takes the surface waters across the climatic zones relatively slowly, from 3 to 7 km per day. This permits the surface waters to adjust at least partially to the local climatic conditions, as they flow across the climatic zones. By their transport of colder water toward the tropics, eastern boundary currents such as the **Peru** or **Benguela currents** also play a role in the global transport of heat.

The Trade Wind belts border the tropics on the north and south (Fig. 7-2). These highly persistent winds drive the **North** and **South Equatorial Currents** westward (Fig. 7-1). One explanation for the **Equatorial Counter Current** is that it is the partial return or eastward flow of water carried westward by the North and South Equatorial Currents. This return flow occurs in the Doldrums, where the surface winds are weaker.

The Southeast Trade Winds of the Southern Hemisphere extend across the equator into the Northern Hemisphere. The Doldrums, separating the

Trade Wind systems of the Northern and Southern Hemispheres, lies generally north of the equator. Consequently the eastward flowing Equatorial Counter Current, separating the current systems of the two hemispheres, lies just north of the equator. The South Equatorial Current actually crosses the equator in the Atlantic and to a lesser extent in the Pacific Ocean.

CORIOLIS EFFECT

Surface waters or pieces of sea ice, set in motion by the wind, move obliquely to the right of the wind in the Northern Hemisphere, and to the left of the wind in the Southern Hemisphere (Fig. 7-3). Caused by the

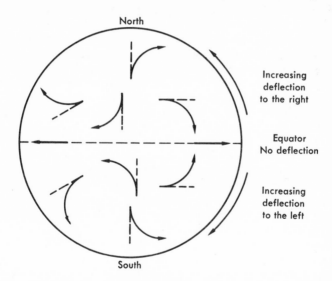

Fig. 7-3. The paths of moving objects are deflected by the Coriolis effect. There is no deflection at the equator; the deflection increases toward the poles. (After A. N. Strahler, *Physical Geography*, 2d ed., [New York: John Wily and Sons, Inc., 1960], p. 129.)

earth's rotation toward the east, this deflection of objects moving long distances over the earth plays a major role in shaping the ocean currents.

A particle moving from the equator toward the pole moves eastward at approximately 1,700 kilometers per hour because of the earth's eastward rotation. After moving northward to latitude 30° (approximate latitude of New Orleans), a particle not attached to the earth's surface still tends to move eastward at 1,700 kilometers per hour. But at New Orleans, the earth's surface is moving eastward at approximately 1,500 kilometers per hour. Thus the particle is now moving eastward faster than the earth's surface at that point. To an observer following the particle's movement from the ground in New Orleans, the particle has apparently been deflected eastward (to the right of the particle's path). An observer on the moon, however, could see that the particle has actually moved in a straight line, but the earth's surface at different latitudes moves eastward at different speeds.

This apparent deflection of the particle is called the **Coriolis effect.** *The Coriolis effect causes the apparent deflection of a moving particle, to the right in the Northern Hemisphere, to the left in the Southern Hemisphere.* The amount of deflection depends on the speed of particle movement and on the latitude. It is zero at the equator, a maximum at the poles. A particle at rest is not affected, nor is a particle moving exactly east-west along the equator (Fig. 7-3).

The Coriolis effect becomes important when the other forces acting on a moving particle are small, and when the particle has moved a long distance. Your automobile is not deflected by the Coriolis effect because it is in contact with the earth's surface. But the deflecting effect plays a major role controlling the movements of winds or ocean currents, or rockets fired long distances.

EKMAN SPIRAL

A wind blowing steadily across the ocean surface sets the water in motion by dragging on the water surface. Wind ripples or waves seem to be responsible for the roughness of the water surface necessary for the wind to set the surface water in motion. A steady wind blowing for 12 hours with an average speed of 100 centimeters per second over deep water causes ocean surface currents of approximately 2 centimeters per second. In other words, the resulting ocean current has a speed which is rather variable but averages about 2 per cent of the speed of the wind that set the water in motion.

Winds cause the surface water to move, but the resulting currents commonly involve water movements extending at least 100 meters below the surface. Thus, we must determine how the energy of the wind-moved surface layer is transmitted downward into the water.

Slowly moving fluids may flow as thin sheets sliding over each other; this is called **laminar flow.** Because of viscosity (or internal friction) each moving fluid layer drags on adjacent layers. At these slow speeds, momentum is transmitted from one layer to another by collisions of individual particles. Thus momentum is transferred from rapidly moving layers to slowly moving layers. We refer to this resistance to flow as **molecular viscosity.**

Ocean waters commonly move too rapidly for laminar flow to persist. Instead, ocean flow is usually **turbulent.** Water particles move in irregular, ever-changing eddies which are carried along by the main flow. The eddies interact, transferring momentum from one eddy to another. The resistance to flow resulting from these interactions is known as **eddy viscosity.**

Eddies are important in the oceans. Transfer of momentum between eddies is many thousand times more rapid than the transfer between molecules. Molecular viscosity changes only slightly with changes in temperature. Eddy viscosity varies greatly depending on the density stratification and speed of flow.

Once set in motion, water particles are deflected by the Coriolis effect. Hence the Coriolis effect must be combined with viscosity and the wind effects to enable us to understand the behavior of wind-induced surface currents.

Theoretical studies have considered the effect of a steady wind blowing across an infinite homogeneous ocean with uniform eddy viscosity. In the Northern Hemisphere of such an idealized ocean, *the surface water layer moves at an angle of 45° to the right of the wind (45° to the left in the Southern Hemisphere).* Each moving layer of water sets the layer below in motion because of viscosity. As each deeper layer is set in motion it is also deflected by the Coriolis effect, causing it to move to the right of the overlying layer. Also the deeper layers move more slowly because momentum is lost in each transfer between layers.

We plot the direction of water movement by an arrow, whose length represents the speed. Fig. 7-4 shows the change in direction and speed

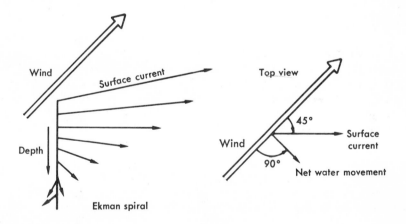

Fig. 7-4. Water movements in a wind-generated current in the Northern Hemisphere.

with depth in a wind-driven current in the Northern Hemisphere. This idealized current pattern has been called the **Ekman spiral,** after the physicist who first pointed out its existence. We can draw a similar one for the Southern Hemisphere by remembering the change in direction of the Coriolis effect.

Because of the deflection of each layer to the right of the overlying layers, the direction of water movement shifts with increasing depth. In fact, at a certain depth, often around 100 meters, the water is moving very slowly in a direction exactly opposite to the surface layer. This depth where the water movements are reversed is considered to be the base of the wind-driven surface current. The Ekman spiral has been produced in the laboratory using rotating models and has been observed in the atmosphere. It is difficult to observe it directly in the oceans, but it is possible to observe some of the effects of the Ekman spiral.

Combining the water movements of all layers in the idealized Ekman spiral, we find that the net water movement is perpendicular to the wind direction (Fig. 7-4). *The net water movement is 90° to the right of the wind in the Northern Hemisphere, 90° to the left in the Southern Hemisphere.* This wind-induced water transport plays an important role in the ocean surface circulation.

The theoretical model we have considered is an idealized or limiting case, calculated for an·infinite, homogenous ocean (no pycnocline and no boundaries). Since no ocean actually satisfies all these conditions, actual wind-induced water movements may differ appreciably from the predictions based on our idealized model. For example, the angle between the directions of wind and surface-water movements varies from 15° in shallow coastal waters to the theoretical maximum of 45° in the deep ocean.

GEOSTROPHIC CURRENTS

Let us examine the surface water movements caused by the nearly circular pattern of the prevailing winds shown in Fig. 7-2. Remember that in deep water the net water movement in the Northern Hemisphere is directed at 90° to the right of the wind (Fig. 7-4). Thus the prevailing winds tend to move the surface water (the least dense water) toward the center of the ocean (Fig. 7-5). These surface wind-induced water move-

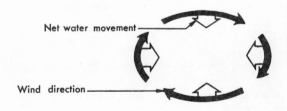

Net water movement

Wind direction

Fig. 7-5.   Net water movement resulting from a nearly closed wind system in the Northern Hemisphere.

ments result in a low "hill" of less dense water near the center of the wind gyre.

The resulting sea-surface topography is very gentle (Fig. 7-6). In the North Pacific Ocean near Japan, the highest elevation (above an arbitrary

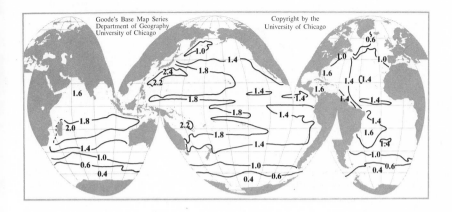

Fig. 7-6. Sea surface topography (in meters) above an arbitrary surface. (After Henry Stommel, "Summary Charts of the Mean Dynamic Topography and Current Field at the Surface of the Ocean, and Related Functions of the Mean Wind-Stress," *Studies on Oceanography*. Edited by Kozo Yoshida [Seattle: University of Washington Press, 1964], p. 54. Reprinted by permission. All rights reserved.)

level surface) is 2.4 m. The lowest sea surface elevations, 0.4 m, occur near Antarctica. The total relief of 2 m is developed on an ocean surface extending many thousands of kilometers. Note that the highest elevations occur near the western ocean boundaries in all oceans.

These "hills" of water are much too small to be measured directly, as we might survey a hill on land. Instead, oceanographers determine the surface topography from the density distribution of the water. We know that the less-dense water flows on the denser, deeper water. From accurate measurements of salinity and temperature, oceanographers compute the distribution of density at any given location.

From this density distribution, an oceanographer can compute the height of the sea surface above an arbitrary level, at a depth in the ocean where the mass of the overlying water is everywhere the same. It is usually assumed that the water in this deep layer is not moving.

Remember that less-dense water occupies more space per gram than denser water. Two water columns of equal mass beneath one square meter will have surfaces at different heights above our chosen surface. The sea surface above the less-dense water will stand higher than the surface above the denser water. Because of this, the sea surface topography can be computed from a knowledge of the distribution of temperature and salinity. *Knowing the sea surface topography, an oceanographer can estimate the current direction and speed.*

To see how this happens, let us consider the water movements resulting from this sea surface topography (Fig. 7-7). A bit of water at the top of such a hill tends to flow downhill under the influence of gravity. After the water begins to move, it is deflected by the Coriolis effect, acting at right

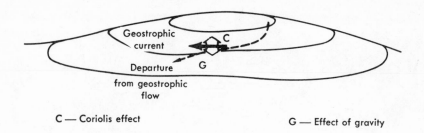

C — Coriolis effect   G — Effect of gravity

Fig. 7-7. **Geostrophic current resulting from a sloping sea surface and the balance between the effect of gravity and the deflection (to the right in the Northern Hemisphere) due to the Coriolis effect. (Modified after W. S. von Arx, *An Introduction to Physical Oceanography*, [Reading, Mass.: Addison-Wesley Publishing Company, Inc., 1962], p. 96.)**

angles to the water movement. Thus, two forces act on the water parcel. Gravity acts in a downhill direction, and the Coriolis effect acts at right angles to the water movement.

The water movement changes direction until the Coriolis effect and the effect of gravity balance each other. *In an idealized, frictionless ocean, gravity acting in a downhill direction would be balanced by the Coriolis effect acting to the right (uphill in an equilibrium situation) resulting in a geostrophic (earth-turned) current.* In the Northern Hemisphere, the hill of less-dense water is on the right when looking in the direction of current flow. The less-dense water is on the left in the Southern Hemisphere. *Oceanographers assume that the major ocean currents are geostrophic currents.* This means that the current directions can be determined from a chart of sea surface topography. The currents will tend to flow around the elevations or depressions. The steepness of the slopes indicates the current speed. The current speed will be greater on a steeper slope, less on a more gentle slope.

In an idealized ocean, where water had no viscosity, the current would flow at a constant elevation around the hill of water. In other words, the water would never reach the bottom of the hill. However sea water does have viscosity, and energy must be expended to keep the water flowing. The water gains the necessary energy by flowing slightly downhill, eventually reaching the bottom. Comparison of the predicted geostrophic currents with the actual drift of icebergs or floating debris from wrecked ships has shown that the geostrophic approximation is a useful, if not exact, technique to study ocean currents.

WIND-INDUCED VERTICAL WATER MOVEMENTS

In addition to horizontal water movements, or currents, winds also cause vertical movements of surface water. Upward (**upwelling**) or downward (**sinking**) water movements can be caused by wind effects.

Coastal upwelling or sinking is common where the prevailing winds tend to blow parallel to the coast. The wind causes the surface water to move. The direction depends on the hemisphere (Northern or Southern) and the wind direction (Fig. 7-8). The presence of the continent and

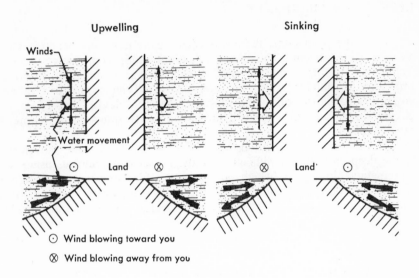

Fig. 7-8. Wind-induced coastal upwelling and sinking, Northern Hemisphere. (After W. S. von Arx, *An Introduction to Physical Oceanography.* [Reading, Mass.: Addison-Wesley Publishing Company, Inc., 1962], p. 115.)

shallow bottom restrict the resulting water movement. When the net wind-induced water movement is directed off-shore, subsurface water flows to the surface near the coast. This slow upward flow, from 100-200 m deep, replaces the surface waters blown seaward. Coastal upwelling is common along parts of the western coasts of all continents. Cool summer weather with frequent fog results chiefly from upwelling of cooler subsurface water. The upwelled waters are depleted in dissolved oxygen because they have not recently been in contact with the atmosphere.

Vertical water movements bring to the sea surface dissolved substances (Fig. 5-1) to support the abundant growth of phytoplankton. Hence, areas of upwelling commonly support extensive populations of fish.

Extensive upwelling also occurs along the equator in the open ocean. This wind-induced upwelling is caused by the change in direction of the Coriolis effect at the equator. The westward-flowing, wind-driven surface currents near the equator are deflected northward, on the north side of the equator, southward on the south side. The surface water moving away from the equator is replaced by the upwelling of deeper water.

Downward movements of coastal waters occur when the wind-induced movement of surface water is shoreward. The effects of coastal sinking are less obvious to coastal dwellers than those of upwelling. However, the local abundance and distribution of fish may be changed radically by coastal sinking of surface waters.

DEEP-OCEAN CIRCULATION

Below the pycnocline, the deep-ocean waters move erratically in sluggishly moving currents. This deep circulation, almost completely separated by the pycnocline from the wind-driven surface circulation, is driven primarily by differences in sea-water density. Temperature and salinity are primary factors controlling sea-water density. Hence, the deep-ocean circulation is frequently called a **thermohaline (thermo** — heat, **haline** — salt) **circulation.**

The deep-ocean circulation is not well-known. Slow water movements of the deep currents are difficult to study. Direct measurements using current meters (Fig. 7-9), which operate much like anemometers in atmospheric studies, require long measurement times and are very expensive to make. For the deep currents we have no counterpart for the information

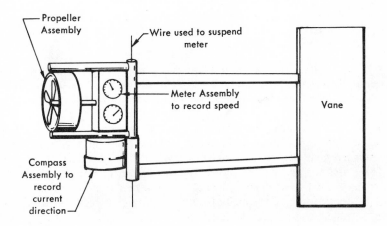

Fig. 7-9. Ekman current meter used to make direct measurements of current direction and speed.

obtained from compiling deflections of ships' courses by surface currents. Instead, much of our knowledge of deep-ocean currents comes from the subsurface distributions of temperature, salinity, and dissolved oxygen. From the distributions of these properties (Fig. 7-10), the general direction of subsurface currents can be deduced (Fig. 7-11).

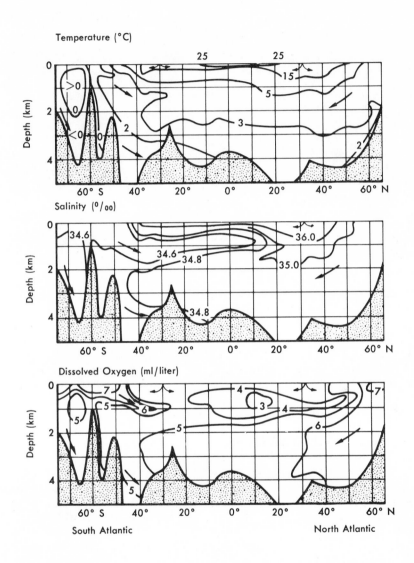

Fig. 7-10. Vertical sections showing distribution of temperature (°C), salinity (‰), and dissolved oxygen (milliliters/liter) in the Western Atlantic Ocean (After Wüst.) Arrows show apparent movement of subsurface waters. (After H. U. Sverdrup, M. W. Johnson, and R. H. Fleming, *The Oceans: Their Physics, Chemistry, and General Biology.* [Englewood Cliffs, N. J.: Prentice-Hall, Inc., 1942], p. 748.)

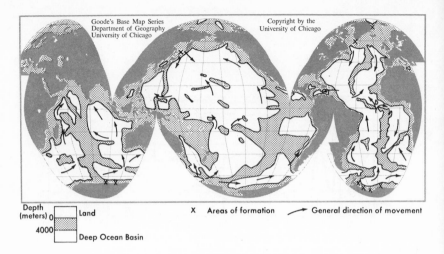

Depth
(meters) 0 ▢ Land   X   Areas of formation   ↗ General direction of movement
4000 ▢
     ▢ Deep Ocean Basin

Fig. 7-11. **Movements of bottom waters. The deep ocean (unshaded) is bounded by the 4,000 m-contour.**

The cold water masses which fill deep-ocean basins form primarily in the polar oceans, especially near Antarctica. In these cold areas, the surface waters are strongly cooled. Where water temperatures are low enough (see Fig. 5-4), sea ice forms. Sea salts are excluded from the ice and mix with the already cold water. The pronounced cooling and increased salinity cause the water density to increase. The resulting cold, dense sea water sinks along the Antarctic continental shelf and slope to reach the sea floor. On the sea floor, the bottom water becomes involved in a bottom current circling Antarctica (Fig. 7-11).

The dense cold water mixes with adjacent water masses while flowing part or all the way around Antarctica. Hence the resulting **Antarctic Bottom Waters,** which eventually flow northward, are a mixture of waters derived from different sources. The cold ($-0.4°C$) Antarctic Bottom Water ($S = 34.66‰$) is recognized in all three oceans.

Subsurface water masses also form in the North Atlantic and North Pacific Oceans (Fig. 7-11). These sources of dense water are locally important, but they do not affect all the ocean basins as the Antarctic Bottom Water does.

Certain water masses, such as the **North Atlantic Deep Water,** are dense enough to sink to the ocean bottom (Fig. 7-10). There it flows generally southward. Eventually it flows over the still denser Antarctic Bottom Water.

A water mass of intermediate density forms near Antarctica. Denser than the surface waters, it flows northward below the surface. The denser North Atlantic Deep Water and Antarctic Bottom Water occupy positions below it.

It is clear that the movement of deep-ocean waters is in many ways not comparable to the movement of the surface waters. Instead of the wind-induced movement at the surface, the deeper waters appear to be pushed by the continued (perhaps partly seasonal) formation of new cold, very dense waters in the polar and subpolar oceans. The water mass formed previously is displaced by later-formed bottom waters. Although vastly simplified, this picture presents the essential difference between the surface- and deep-ocean circulations.

After leaving the sea surface, the subsurface waters are isolated from the atmosphere for 500 to 2,000 years on the average. Below the pycnocline, there is little opportunity for the temperature or salinity to change except by mixing with adjacent water masses, or by the very slow movements of molecules known as diffusion. For this reason, *temperature and salinity provide useful tags to trace the movements of deep-ocean water masses.* Dissolved oxygen is depleted by respiration of animals and not replaced. Hence the amount of dissolved oxygen present provides a tracer to help determine the rate and direction of water movement.

It appears that the deep-ocean flow is directed generally north-south (Fig. 7-11). As in the surface circulation, the bottom currents tend to be strongest on the western side of the ocean basin. In contrast to the surface circulation, these bottom currents cross the equator in the Atlantic and Pacific Oceans. The Atlantic Ocean appears to play a very important role in the deep-ocean circulation because it connects the polar regions of the Northern and Southern Hemispheres (Fig. 1-3).

Unlike the surface currents, *the movements of the bottom waters are strongly influenced by the bottom topography.* The location of gaps in the Mid-Atlantic Ridge controls the flow of bottom water from the deep basins of the western Atlantic into the eastern Atlantic basins. The ridge separating the Arctic Sea from the Atlantic Ocean prevents the escape into the Atlantic of dense water masses formed in the Arctic Sea. Only those formed near Greenland can flow into the Atlantic. In short, the effect of the deep-ocean topography on the flow of the bottom currents may be compared to the barrier that a mountain range presents to land travel. To continue the analogy, just as the course of an airplane is not affected by mountains, so the flow of the surface currents is unimpeded by rough terrain on the deep-ocean floor.

The subsurface waters must eventually return to the sea surface. This return flow may be accomplished by the slow upward movement of the deep waters toward the surface in all oceans. Some scientists believe that these waters move upward 2 to 5 m per year, in all oceans. Eventually these former bottom waters pass through the pycnocline. In the surface zone, they are carried by the wind-driven circulation and returned to the surface.

WATER MASSES — THEIR FORMATION AND MIXING

Many of the important water masses — identified by characteristic temperatures and salinities — of the oceans form in the coastal oceans or marginal seas. We have already discussed the formation of cold, dense water masses at high latitudes, and have briefly mentioned that distinctive water masses also form as the result of evaporation and warming of surface waters. For instance, a thin layer of warm, saline water flows out from the Mediterranean Sea through the Strait of Gilbraltar. A similar water mass forms in the Red Sea. Both water masses are recognizable as thin layers of warm, salty water under large areas of the Atlantic and Indian Oceans. Being less dense than the bottom waters, they occur at intermediate depths.

Below the pycnocline in the open ocean, there is relatively little energy available to cause vertical mixing. In this environment, a water parcel — a relatively large volume of water — will tend to move laterally along surfaces of constant density. In a stable situation, the water below will be somewhat denser than any given water parcel; that above will be somewhat less dense. In this situation a water parcel will tend to spread and move laterally, as a thin layer interleaved between other layers.

Obviously, heat, salt, and dissolved gases can move across boundaries between adjacent layers. If the individual layers are thin, each layer will gradually lose its identity. Doubtlessly many of the water masses in the deep ocean have formed through such mixing processes acting over many years. Using closely spaced measurements of temperature and salinity, physical oceanographers have shown that layers formed by such mixing can be identified in the deep waters of the North Atlantic Ocean. This formation and movement of water masses in thin, nearly horizontal layers is characteristic of the deep open ocean. As often stated, *it is easier to move than to mix water masses in the deep ocean.*

Energy for mixing processes is supplied (1) at the sea surface and (2) near the sea floor. The winds supply energy for mixing at the sea surface. The nearly isothermal (or isohaline) surface zone, often tens of meters thick, is normally a result of wind-induced mixing. Density changes resulting from surface cooling of highly saline waters can cause mixing through the sinking of these denser waters.

Water flow near the ocean bottom also causes mixing. Such mixing is especially noticeable when strong currents flow across an obstruction such as a sill or a ridge. In the shallow coastal oceans, such bottom-associated mixing becomes relatively more important.

Near the coasts, strong tides and currents supply relatively large amounts of energy for mixing, as do the breakers in the surf zone. Fresh water discharged by rivers is mixed with sea water near the continental margins. This is the opposite of evaporation — separation of fresh water from salt water — which occurs over most of the ocean.

In summary, *mixing is a consequence of the continual movement of water in the ocean.* As we have seen, water movement occurs in the ocean on all scales. Individual water molecules are constantly moving and are, in turn, carried by eddies. Eddies are transported by currents. Such swirling movements cause the transfer of heat, salt, or other properties. By such processes, the properties of individual water parcels are mixed to form distinct water masses.

If a water parcel is small and far from energy sources, the molecular motions may cause the transfer of heat, salt or other properties. If somewhat larger, the ever-present eddies may cause the mixing. Finally, if a water mass is very large, currents will likely play the major role in mixing processes. In general, *mixing results from water motions of the same size or smaller than the water parcel. Water movements on a scale larger than the water parcel will tend to transport the water rather than mix it.*

QUESTIONS

1. Draw a simple current gyre. Label the eastern and western boundary currents and the east-west currents for the North Atlantic Ocean. The South Pacific Ocean.

2. Draw a generalized current pattern in a rectangular ocean, extending from 60°N to 60°S. Label the currents for the Pacific. For the Atlantic.

3. List and briefly discuss the major factors causing the surface water movements in the ocean.

4. Discuss the result of the Coriolis effect acting on surface water movements in the ocean.

5. What is a geostrophic current? Are all ocean currents geostrophic currents? If not, why not?

6. Draw a diagram showing the sloping sea surface associated with a geostrophic current in the Southern Hemisphere.

7. What evidence supports the statement that the circulation of the ocean and atmosphere are closely linked?

8. List the different techniques that can be used to study ocean currents. Which are most satisfactory? Which are least satisfactory? Why?

9. Describe and draw the Ekman spiral for a wind-driven current in the Southern Hemisphere.

10. Draw a schematic profile of the sea surface between 20°N and 20°S across the equator in the Pacific Ocean along 180°E. Show the direction of current flow. (⊙ current flowing toward you, ⊗ current flowing away from you.)

11. Draw a schematic east-west profile of the sea surface in the Atlantic Ocean through the Sargasso Sea (30°N). Show the current directions.

SUPPLEMENTARY READING

Knauss, J. A., "The Cromwell Current," *Scientific American,* April, 1961.

McDonald, J. E., "The Coriolis Effect," *Scientific American,* May, 1952.

Munk, W., "The Circulation of the Oceans," *Scientific American,* September, 1955.

Posner, G. S., "The Peru Current," *Scientific American,* March, 1954.

Starr, V. P., "The General Circulation of the Atmosphere," *Scientific American,* December, 1956.

Chapter 8

Waves and Tides

The sea surface is rarely still. Surface disturbances, called waves, cross it continuously carrying energy. Any disturbance, such as a pebble dropped into the water or a submarine land slide, can generate a wave. *The wind, earthquakes, and the gravitational attraction of the moon and sun are the three most important wave generators.*

Winds cause most of the waves commonly observed on the oceans. These waves range from ripples less than a centimeter high to giant storm-generated waves more than 30 meters high. Their character is easily observed. Tides also behave like waves but are so large that their wave-like characteristics are easily overlooked. Seismic sea waves, caused by earthquakes, often result in spectacular waves causing catastrophic property damage and loss of life, especially in lands bordering the Pacific Ocean.

IDEAL PROGRESSIVE WAVES

We will start with a group of simple sea waves (a **wave train**) to study the parts of a wave (Fig. 8-1). Watching a series of such **progressive waves** pass a fixed point, such as a piling, we see a regular succession of **crests** — the highest part of a wave — and **troughs** — the lowest part of a wave. The **wave height** *(H)* is the vertical distance from a crest to a trough. Successive crests (or troughs) are separated by one **wave length** *(L)*. The time required for successive crests (or troughs) to pass our fixed point is the **wave period** *(T)* commonly expressed in seconds. The wave period is easily measured and frequently used to classify waves.

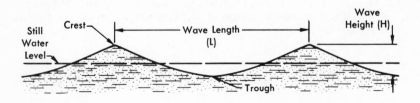

Fig. 8-1. Simple sea wave and its parts.

Wave speed *(V)* can be calculated by $V = L/T$. This simple formula tells us that the wave speed, wave length, and wave period are related, so that knowing any two factors we can calculate the third. The wave height is not related to the other three factors and must be determined by observation. The wave steepness is the ratio of wave height to wave length and may be expressed as *H/L*.

Observing a chip floating on the water surface we find that it moves forward on each wave crest and backward in the wave trough. After the passage of each complete wave, it returns to its initial position. This demonstrates that only the wave form is moving; there is little net water movement associated with the passage of such a wave in deep water.

By observing the movement of several small markers floating at various depths in a tank, we see that the markers and the water move in nearly circular vertical orbits as waves pass (Fig. 8-2). The diameter of the orbits

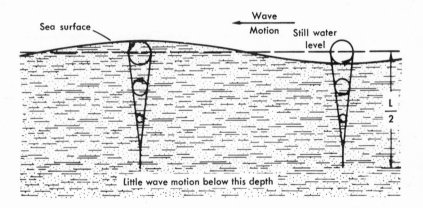

Fig. 8-2. Wave profile and orbital motions in deep-water waves. Note the diminishing size of the orbits with increasing depth below the surface.

is equal to the wave height. Beneath the wave crest, the orbital motion is momentarily in the direction of wave motion. In the wave troughs, the orbital motion is reversed.

The speed or orbital motion decreases and the orbits become smaller away from the surface. At a depth of half a wave length *(L/2)* the orbital motion has nearly vanished. Thus the wave-generated circular water movements occur only near the surface in the deep ocean.

Water particles move slightly faster in the wave crests than in the wave troughs. Hence there is a slight net movement of water in the direction of wave travel. The water movement is much slower, however, than the wave speed, and we can ignore it for our purposes. This wave-induced net motion should not be confused with the wind-induced water movement causing the ocean currents.

Where the water depth is less than half a wave length, the nearness of the bottom interferes with the orbital motions. Water particles very near

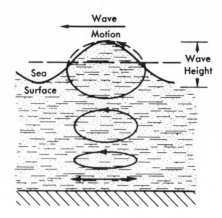

Fig. 8-3. **Motions of water particles caused by shallow-water waves.**

the bottom cannot move vertically, and thus move only horizontally (Fig. 8-3). Further from the bottom, the water particles move in elliptical orbits which become flatter near the bottom and more circular near the surface.

Waves are not influenced by the ocean bottom where the water depth is greater than half the wave length. Therefore in the deep ocean the wave speed is determined by the wave length and period, and the longer waves travel faster than the shorter waves. *Long waves from a distant storm arrive first, followed by the shorter waves.*

In shallow water the speed of the waves may be controlled by the water depth. Where the water depth is less than one-twentieth of the wave length $(L/20)$, wave speed (V), in meters per second, can be calculated by $V = 3.1 \sqrt{d}$, where d is the average water depth in meters. As waves move from deep to shallow water, wave speed and wave length change, but the wave period does not.

SEISMIC SEA WAVES (TSUNAMIS)

Some of the largest ocean waves are generated by sudden movements of the ocean bottom. Crustal movements caused by earthquakes or slumping of sediment can cause large waves to form. These **seismic sea waves***, or tsunamis, have wave lengths up to 200 kilometers, periods of 10 to 20 minutes, and wave heights up to 0.5 meters in the deep ocean.

Unnoticed by ships on the open sea, the seismic sea waves may form huge breakers when they encounter the proper bottom configuration in shallow water. Large loss of life and extensive property damage has re-

---

*Also erroneously called tidal waves. They are unrelated to tidal phenomena.

sulted as the aftermath of a distant large earthquake. The Japanese and the Hawaiian Islands are especially prone to these catastrophic waves.

WIND WAVES

Wind waves are formed in many sizes and are doubtlessly the most familiar type of ocean wave. They are yet another manifestation of the winds blowing across the ocean and transferring energy to the surface zone. Wind waves are an important factor in the near-surface ocean, causing mixing, as well as promoting evaporation and exchange of atmospheric gases across the water surface. As we have seen, wave mixing controls the thermocline depth in many parts of the ocean.

When the wind begins to blow across a still water surface, it first sets up small wavelets or **ripples,** usually less than one centimeter high. The ripples have rounded crests and V-shaped troughs. Because of their small size, **surface tension** — resulting from the mutual attractions of the water molecules — plays an important role. Such waves are called **capillary waves.** These ripples are very numerous; they move with the wind and last only a very short time. Many scientists believe that the ripples provide much of the wind's "grip" on the water, permitting wave formation as well as wind-induced currents.

As the wind strength increases, small waves are formed which also travel with the wind. These are called **gravity waves.** The size of the waves formed depends on the wind speed, the length of time it blows in one direction, and the distance the wind has blown across the water. This distance is commonly known as the **fetch** (Fig. 8-4). In short, *the size of the waves depends on the amount of energy imparted to the water by the wind.*

In a storm or strong wind, a complicated mixture of superimposed waves and ripples develops, known as a **sea.** The waves continue to grow until they are as large as a wind of that speed can generate. After the wind dies, the waves continue to travel away from the generating area. After leaving the generating area, the waves change, becoming more regular. These long, regular waves outside the generating area are known as **swell** (Fig. 8-4). Much of the energy in ocean waves is transmitted by the sea and the swell.

Unlike the wind-generated currents, wind waves are little affected by the Coriolis effect, because only limited water movements are involved in wave propagation. Waves tend to move in the same direction as the wind that generated them. A wind from a different direction may destroy a preexisting wave pattern and generate a new one in its place. Little energy is lost crossing the deep ocean, and the waves continue until they meet an obstacle such as a continental shore where their energy is dissipated in the surf.

Wind waves may be classified according to their period. Ripples have periods of a fraction of a second. Wind waves in fully developed seas have periods up to fifteen seconds; swell has a period of from five to sixteen seconds.

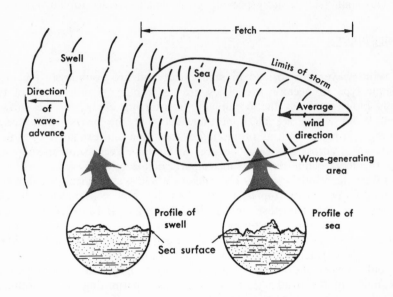

Fig. 8-4. Schematic diagram showing development of wind waves in a storm area and the changes as the sea evolves into swell as the waves travel out of the wave-generating area.

As waves approach the beach, the orbital motion of the water particles is influenced by the bottom as the water becomes more shallow, less than $L/2$ in depth. Although the wave period remains unchanged, the wave length is shortened. As a result, the wave height increases and the wave crests become more peaked. The **wave steepness** (H/L) increases until it reaches a critical value, about $1/7$. At this point, the wave crest peaks sharply, becomes unstable, and breaks (Fig. 8-5).

Waves break when there is insufficient water in the trough to support the wave crests as the water particles move forward. The water in the crest is thus unsupported as it moves forward in its orbit, and the wave front collapses. Waves usually break when the water depth is 1.3 times the wave height.

The energy of a breaking wave frequently causes a new set of smaller waves to form. These waves also break when they reach shallower water. Thus the surf zone may have several sets of breakers, depending on wave conditions and nearshore bottom configuration.

When the waves break they expend their energy through the turbulence of the water and by washing up on the beach. In these final stages, the wave's energy is changed to heat energy. If this heat energy were not thoroughly mixed through many meters of sea water, it would cause an appreciable temperature rise in the surf zone.

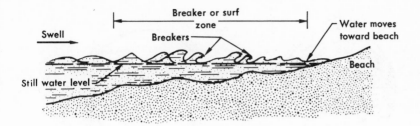

Fig. 8-5. **Swell peaks upon entering shallow water. At a depth of 1.3 times the wave height, the wave breaks, then reforms and breaks again. Finally, the water itself moves toward the beach. (After U.S. Army Coastal Engineering Research Center,** *Shore Protection, Planning and Design,* **Technical Report No. 4. Third edition [1966], p. A-43.)**

TIDES

Of all the ocean phenomena, the **tides** — the periodic rise and fall of the sea surface — are probably the easiest to observe. A firmly anchored piling marked in meters (or feet) can be used to measure the relative height of the tide. By recording the height of the tide at frequent intervals, one can obtain a good record of the tide during the period of observation. Even an automatic tide gauge is a simple device. A float is coupled by wires to a pencil which draws the tidal curve on a paper-covered, clock-driven cylinder.

Known since antiquity, tides were first satisfactorily explained by the work of Sir Isaac Newton (1642-1727). His law of gravitational attraction states that the attraction between two bodies is directly proportional to the product of their masses and inversely proportional to the square of the distance between them. Hence all the celestial bodies affect the ocean waters to some degree because of their mutual gravitational attraction. To understand ocean tides we will consider only the gravitational effects of the sun and moon. These are important because of their large mass (the sun) and nearness to the earth (the moon).

The earth and the moon strongly attract each other because of their proximity. This mutual attraction is balanced by the centrifugal force resulting from their rotation about the center of the earth-moon system. In fact, the earth and moon may be considered as twin planets revolving around a mutual center about 4,700 kilometers from the earth's center. Thus, both are affected by centrifugal forces arising from the revolution around this common center.

Although the centrifugal force exactly balances the gravitational attraction at the centers of the earth and the moon, the two forces do not cancel everywhere on the surfaces of the two bodies (Fig. 8-6). On the side of the earth nearest the moon, the moon's gravitational pull is greater than

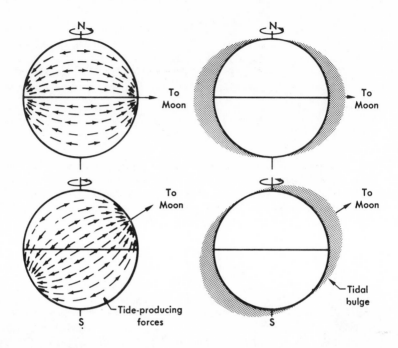

Fig. 8-6. **Tide-producing force and resulting tidal bulges on an ocean-covered earth with the moon in the plane of the earth's equator (upper) and above the plane of the equator (lower).**

the centrifugal force. On the opposite side of the earth, the centrifugal force exceeds the moon's attraction. Although the actual forces involved are small, they are strong enough to cause water movements. On a smooth, water-covered earth, the water would flow towards the moon on one side of the earth, away from the moon on the other. This would form two tidal bulges or crests separated by a low area, or trough. The height of these tidal bulges would be controlled by the balance attraction of the tide-generating forces and the earth's gravity pulling the water back toward the earth.

The moon is the dominant factor controlling the period and height of the tide. The sun's great mass, however, causes it to have an appreciable effect on ocean tides in spite of its great distance from the earth. The average solar tide is about half as high as the average lunar tide. Both the sun and the moon also cause slight but measurable tides in the solid earth, which we will not discuss here.

The moon passes over the meridian of longitude at a given location on earth once every 24 hours, 50 minutes. On an idealized water-covered earth, any given point on its surface would pass beneath the two tidal crests (high water) and two tidal troughs (low water) during each **tidal day** of 24 hours, 50 minutes. The elapsed time between successive high or low waters is called the **tidal period.**

If the moon were in the plane of the earth's equator, the two high waters at each location would be equal. However the moon's position (and associated tidal bulges) may shift from 28.5° north of the earth's equator to 28.5° south of the earth's equator, changing the relative heights of high and low waters at any given point. This is but one of many complicating factors involved in tidal phenomena.

At certain times during the moon's travel around the earth, the direction of its gravitational pull is aligned with the sun's. At these times — near the time of new and full moons — the two tide-producing bodies act together (Fig. 8-7). Thus the resulting tidal bulges, or crests, are higher

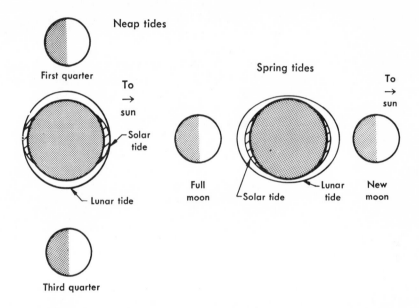

Fig. 8-7. Relationship of the moon and sun to the earth during the spring and neap tides. (After Willard Bascom, *Waves and Beaches: The Dynamics of the Ocean Surface.* [Garden City, N. Y.: Anchor Books, Doubleday and Company, Inc., 1964], p. 86. Copyright © 1964 by Education Services. Reprinted by permission of Doubleday and Company, Inc.)

and the water level between them in the tidal troughs is the lowest. These are the **spring tides,** when the **daily tidal range** — the vertical distance between high and low tides — is largest. Near the time of the first and third quarters of the moon, the solar and lunar tides do not coincide, and the daily tidal range is the least. These are called the **neap tides.**

This simple picture, or **equilibrium model** of the tides, first presented by Newton, explains the relative effects of the sun and moon on ocean tides. It also explains why there are usually two high and two low waters each tidal day. It fails to predict, however, two important aspects of the tides — their height and the time of high or low tide relative to the moon's passage overhead.

Let us first consider the timing of high water. The simple equilibrium model predicts that high water will occur when the moon is highest in the sky above our position or directly below our position. This would require that each tidal bulge travel at a speed of approximately 1,600 kilometers per hour (relative to the earth's surface) to keep pace with the moon's travel overhead.

We can also consider the tides to be very long waves. The two tidal bulges, or crests, occur on opposite sides of the earth, hence the tides have wave length of nearly 22,000 kilometers. We know that the oceans are slightly less than 4 kilometers deep on the average, so that the ratio of wave length to ocean depth is 22,000/4. Thus, the tidal wave in the ocean must behave like a shallow-water wave because the ratio is much less than $L/20$, the limit for shallow-water waves.

For the tidal wave to travel fast enough to keep up with the moon, the oceans would need to be at least 22 kilometers deep. Consequently, the tidal crests are displaced from their equilibrium position by the frictional drag on the ocean bottom and the earth's rotation (Fig. 8-8).

The height of the tide at a given location is a very complicated matter. It depends not only on the depth but on the shape of the ocean and the connection of the local water body with the world ocean.

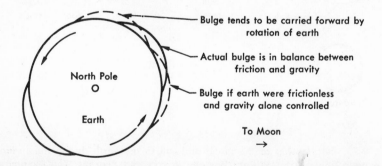

Fig. 8-8. Position of the tidal bulge is determined by the equilibrium between the gravitational attraction of the moon and the frictional drag on a rotating earth. (After Willard Bascom, *Waves and Beaches: The Dynamics of the Ocean Surface.* [Garden City, N. Y.: Anchor Books, Doubleday and Company, Inc., 1964], p. 87. Copyright © 1964 by Education Services. Reprinted by permission of Doubleday and Company, Inc.)

TYPES OF TIDES

Years of tidal observations have shown that three different types of tides may be distinguished. The **diurnal tide** — one high and one low water

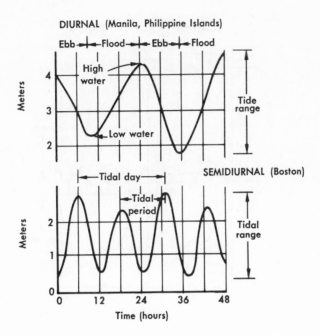

Fig. 8-9. Diurnal and semidiurnal types of tides.

per tidal day — is the simplest type of tide (Fig. 8-9). This type of tide is common in parts of the northern Gulf of Mexico and Southeast Asia.

Semidiurnal tides — two high waters and two low waters per tidal day (Fig. 8-9) — are common on the Atlantic coasts of the United States and Europe. Note that successive high water stands and low water stands are approximately equal. (The **stand** of the tide is the time during which there is no appreciable change in water level.) This is the type of tide predicted by the simple equilibrium model of the tides.

Along the Pacific coast of the United States the **mixed tide** is most common. Successive high water and low water stands differ appreciably (Fig. 8-10). Here we have **higher high water** and **lower high water,** as well as **higher low water** and **lower low water.**

We have considered only the most important factors affecting the tides. The complexity of tidal phenomena can be seen in the tidal curves (Fig. 8-11) for one month at New York (semidiurnal tide) and Seattle (mixed tide). The tides have engaged the attention of many of the best mathematicians, physicists, and oceanographers. Their prediction at coastal points is still primarily based upon detailed analyses of observations made over a long time at each port. Nonetheless, tidal predictions are perhaps the best example of successful prediction of oceanic phenomena.

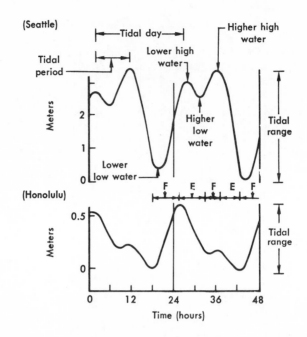

Fig. 8-10. **Examples of the mixed type of tide. F — flood current. E — ebb current.**

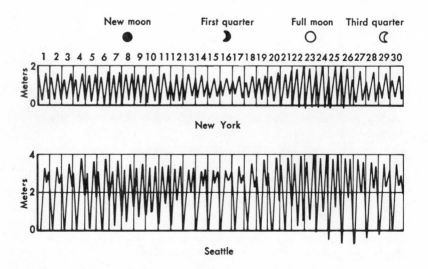

Fig. 8-11. **Tidal variations during one month.**

TIDAL CURRENTS

Like other shallow-water waves, the rise and fall of the tides cause horizontal water movements, known as **tidal currents.** In the open ocean, away from obstructions, tidal currents constantly change direction (Fig. 8-12) and are known as **rotary currents.** The currents repeat the cycle once in each tidal period.

Near the shore or in rivers or harbors, the coast obstructs the tidal currents, preventing the rotary motion observed in the open ocean. Here we observe the familiar **reversing tidal currents.** The currents flow in one direction during parts of the tidal cycle, and reverse their flow during other parts (Fig. 8-13).

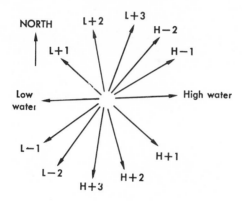

Fig. 8-12. Hourly direction and speed of tidal currents during one tidal period at Nantucket Shoals Lightship off the New England coast. Times are shown in hours before and after low and high waters. (After U. S. Naval Oceanographic Office, *American Practical Navigator.* **H. O. Pub. 9 [Washington, D. C., 1958], p. 712.)**

When the water level is rising in a harbor (Fig. 8-9, 8-10), water must flow toward the land. These tidal currents flowing shoreward (upstream in coastal rivers or estuaries) are called **flood currents.** As the tide goes out and sea level falls, water must flow seaward. Seaward currents (downstream in coastal rivers or estuaries) are called **ebb currents.** Periods of **slack water** — little or no current — separate the ebb and flood current (Fig. 8-13).

Prediction of tidal currents is also a complicated and largely empirical matter. Tidal currents are affected by non-tidal water movements, such as river flow. Also, the time and speed of maximum flood or ebb current may vary widely within a single bay or harbor. Tidal current tables contain predictions of these currents, usually based on long series of observa-

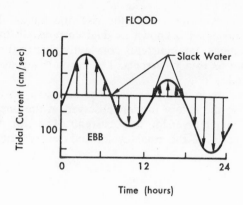

Fig. 8-13. Tidal currents at Admiralty Inlet, Puget Sound, Washington. (After U. S. Naval Oceanographic Office, *American Practical Navigator.* H. O. Pub. 9 [Washington, D. C., 1958], p. 712.)

tions. Correction factors are given to correct for the local variations in time and speed of these currents.

IDEAL STATIONARY WAVES

From our discussion of the tides, we can see that tidal phenomena have many characteristics similar to progressive waves. There is yet another type of wave that plays an important role in tidal phenomena in many regions. This is the **stationary wave,** also known as a **standing wave** or **seiche** (pronounced sāsh) when it occurs in a bay or lake. Such waves are easily generated in the laboratory by tilting a round-bottomed dish and then setting it down on the table top. Viewed from the side, the surface of the water in the dish can be seen to tilt to one side, then to the other. This familiar type of wave — responsible for the spilling of many a carelessly carried bowl of soup — is distinctly different from the progressive wave previously discussed.

During each oscillation of the water surface, the water surface remains at the same level at certain locations. These are called the **nodes** (Fig. 8-14). The stationary waves generated in our small cup or dish will usually have a single **nodal line** where the water level does not change. It is possible, however, to have several nodal lines or **nodal points** about which the water surface tilts.

The locations of greatest vertical movement of the water surface are called the **antinodes,** or **crests.** Again it is possible to have more than the two crests generated in our simple experiment. Antinodes always occur at the ends of the basin. By placing chips or dye in the water we can observe the water motions generated by the stationary waves. We find that there

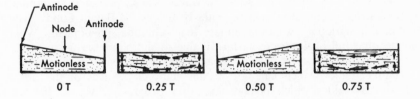

Fig. 8-14. Water motions in a simple stationary wave at quarter-period intervals.

is no water movement when the water surface is tilted the most. The water moves most rapidly when the water surface is horizontal, its equilibrium position.

The largest horizontal water movements occur below the nodal line. Beneath the crests the water movements are entirely vertical. We have none of the circular motions observed in the progressive waves.

Stationary waves may be generated in an enclosed body of water by any sudden disturbance, such as a storm or sudden change in atmospheric pressure. Once set in motion, a water body such as a lake will oscillate with a period determined by the depth and length of the basin. The period *(T)*, in seconds, can be calculated for a rectangular basin by

$$T = \frac{2\,l}{\sqrt{gh}} = 0.64\frac{l}{\sqrt{h}}$$

where the depth *(d)* and length *(l)* are given in meters and g (9.8 m/sec^2) is the acceleration due to gravity.

Periodic rise and fall of the water surface in lakes can be caused by such stationary waves. Lake Erie has such a periodic change of level of 8 centimeters with a period of 14.3 hours. In Lake Michigan the change in level is 7 centimeters with a characteristic period of 6 hours. Because of the earth's rotation, the wave crests in such large water bodies move in a clockwise direction (in the Northern Hemisphere) around the lake or sea. The deflection of the wave crests is caused by the deflection of the relatively large water movements associated with such large stationary waves.

Stationary waves are also generated in the oceans or adjacent seas or estuaries by the astronomical tides. Some of the complications seen in tidal phenomena are due to the tendency of each ocean basin to have stationary waves associated with other tidal phenomena. Each basin has a characteristic period of oscillation determined by the size and configuration of the basin.

Long, narrow seas, such as the Red Sea, or broad, shallow seas, such as the North Sea or the Baltic Sea, have easily recognizable stationary waves. These waves are generated by the periodic rise and fall of the sea surface at their open ends. Those seas or bays whose length and depth are suitable will tend to have stationary waves whose period is determined by the astronomical tides. In such water bodies as the Bay of Fundy, Nova Scotia, the stationary waves dominate the local tidal phenomena. Where the rise and fall of the water surface is due to stationary waves, low water (or high water) comes at nearly the same time in all parts of the bay.

Water bodies which can not sustain stationary waves of the proper periods have tides which behave more like progressive waves. In Puget Sound or Chesapeake Bay, high water or low water progresses from the mouth to the head of the system, taking several hours to do so.

INTERNAL WAVES

Up to this point, we have only considered waves at the air-sea interface. Although these are the most obvious waves in the ocean, they are by no means the only ones.

Waves can and do occur at various subsurface density discontinuities. They may be detected in various ways. A submarine submerged to the depth of a pronounced density discontinuity has been reported to rise and fall as a result of the passage of **internal waves.**

A series of temperature or salinity measurements at an open ocean location often reveals the passage of internal waves. There the internal waves cause periodic shallowing and deepening of water having a characteristic temperature or salinity value. Tidal phenomena seem to cause some internal waves in the ocean, and other forces doubtlessly result in such waves. Internal waves in the oceans are still little understood. This is due in part to the difficulty of making the necessary observations.

QUESTIONS

1. What three processes generate waves in the ocean?
2. List some of the wave characteristics you could use to distinguish sea and swell.
3. Describe the three types of tides.
4. Why do waves break in shallow water?
5. During an eclipse of the moon, would we have spring or neap tides? Why?
6. List some of the factors which cause the observed heights of the tides to differ substantially from predictions made for a water-covered earth.
7. Why is the movement of wind waves little affected by the Coriolis effect?
8. How do the tidal currents in the open ocean differ from those in a coastal estuary?
9. Is a seismic sea wave (height 1 m; length 200 km; period 15 minutes) a shallow-water wave or a deep-water wave? Calculate its speed, assuming that the ocean is uniformly 4 km deep.

SUPPLEMENTARY READING

Bascom, W., "Ocean Waves," *Scientific American*, August, 1959.
————, *Waves and Beaches: The Dynamics of the Ocean Surface*. Garden City, N. Y.: Anchor Books, Doubleday and Company, Inc., 1964. Elementary.
Bernstein, J., "Tsunamis," *Scientific American*, August, 1954.
Defant, Albert, *Ebb and Flow: The Tides of Earth, Air, and Water*. Ann Arbor, Mich.: The University of Michigan Press, 1958. Intermediate in difficulty.
Kinsman, Blair, *Wind Waves: Their Generation and Propagation on the Ocean Surface*. Englewood Cliffs, N. J.: Prentice-Hall, Inc., 1965. Technical.
Marmer, Harry Aaron, *The Tide*. New York: Appleton-Century-Crofts, 1926.
Russell, R. C. H. and D. H. MacMillan, *Waves and Tides*. New York: Philosophical Library, Inc., 1953.
Tricker, R. A. R., *Bores, Breakers, Waves, and Wakes*. New York: American Elsevier Publishing Company, Inc., 1965.

Chapter 9

Shallow and Coastal Oceans

Coastal oceans and adjacent seas are only a small part of the world ocean: 12.5 per cent of the earth's surface, but only about 4 per cent of the ocean's volume. Continental shelf areas alone comprise 5.2 per cent of the earth's surface, but only 0.2 per cent of the ocean volume.

Such figures obscure, however, the true significance to us of this part of the world ocean. Most of our contact with the ocean involves areas lying near the continents. These highly productive waters have long provided much of our sea food. Beaches and coastal waters are important recreational areas. With the continued population expansion and industrial development of coastal areas, the ocean margins increasingly serve as the disposal site for municipal and industrial waste products. Coastal waters are utilized to dilute waste products to acceptable levels for the tidal currents near the coast to disperse them.

Obviously such uses tend to conflict; swimming in polluted waters has limited appeal. Hence it is vitally important that future utilization of the coastal ocean be carefully planned, with regard for the various possible uses. In short, man's future interest in the oceans will likely focus close to the continental margins. In this chapter we consider some of the important processes affecting the coastal oceans and shallow seas.

PHYSICAL CHARACTERISTICS OF THE COASTAL OCEAN

In the open ocean, most processes tend to act over relatively long periods of time. For example, a glass float carried by the surface currents takes several years to cross the North Pacific Ocean. It requires many hundreds to a few thousand years for bottom water to return to the surface after sinking below Antarctic waters. The characteristic time for processes in the open ocean is at least on the order of years, ranging up to a few thousand years.

Near the coasts, ocean processes occur more rapidly. Tidal currents are important, and the tidal period, 12 hours, 25 minutes, is the characteristic time for many processes. Seasonal climatic changes on the adjacent continents also have a major effect on the coastal waters. Such seasonal changes involve not only temperature changes, but also changes in wind patterns and the amounts of precipitation. These climatic regimes lasting four to six months provide the longer framework within which the short term processes operate. Only rarely, as in the monsoon-controlled Northern Indian Ocean, do such seasonal climatic changes affect the open ocean.

Not only are the coastal waters subject to processes acting for a shorter time than is usual in the open ocean, but the distances involved are generally much less. Coastal waters are often isolated to some degree from the open ocean. For example, the Sea of Japan near the coast of Asia (Fig. 1-2) is isolated from the Pacific Ocean by the Japanese Islands. Bays, harbors and fiords obviously have restricted communication with the sea, both vertically and horizontally. Therefore it is not surprising to find that near the coast, surface sea water properties may change radically within distances of a few tens or hundreds of kilometers. This is in distinct contrast to the open ocean where surface-water properties usually change gradually over hundreds or thousands of kilometers.

A major factor controlling processes in the coastal ocean is its shallowness. Continental shelves, with depths less than 200 m, underlie about half of the coastal ocean and adjacent seas. Deep-ocean bottom underlies only about 15 per cent of the area; the continental slope underlies the rest.

Because of the shallowness of the coastal oceans, especially the continental shelves, the overlying waters are strongly influenced by the ocean bottom. Water movements also affect the bottom and its sediment. Most of the wave energy from storms at sea is dissipated in the surf along the coast. This results in sediment movements, mixing of the near-shore waters, and the release of wave energy as heat.

The restrictions on water flow imposed by the coasts cause the rotary tidal currents (Fig. 8-12) of the open ocean to change to reversing tidal currents (Fig. 8-13). The tidal currents associated with the tidal rise and fall of sea level in estuaries and bays play a major role in mixing water and in breaking down the pycnocline. Near the coast the tidal range is larger and the tidal currents are stronger than in the open ocean.

The presence of the coast affects the ocean in yet another way. Wind-induced upwelling along the coast results from the restricted water flow along the coast (Fig. 7-8). In the absence of the coast, only the surface waters would be moved by the longshore winds. Because of the presence of the continent, the water from 100 to 200 m below the surface must move upward to replace surface waters moved seaward by the wind. A similar argument can be made for wind-induced sinking of surface water.

SALINITY AND TEMPERATURE IN COASTAL REGIONS

Large salinity variations are a characteristic feature of surface waters in coastal oceans. In general, surface-water salinity is lowest near the continents, except in areas of wind-induced upwelling. Surface-water salinity is greatest near the center of the ocean current gyres. Belts of equal salinity tend to parallel the coast lines, especially in the North Pacific Ocean (Fig. 6-7).

Variation in temperature is controlled primarily by latitude, distance north or south of the equator, just as it is in the open ocean. The presence of the coast has less influence on surface water temperature than on salinity (Fig. 6-6). Surface temperatures in coastal waters are affected by the boundary currents transporting warm or cold water and by the wind-induced upwelling of cold subsurface waters along certain coasts.

The discharge of large amounts of fresh water from rivers causes localized upwelling. Mixing takes place as deeper water is drawn upward (entrained) by the surface water moving seaward over the underlying denser water. Resulting mixtures of fresh- and sea-water are less dense than the undiluted sea water. Thus, when a bit of sea water mixes with fresh water it becomes less dense and moves toward the surface. This upward movement of deeper water may be called **river-induced upwelling.** It brings nutrient elements (Fig. 5-1) necessary for plant growth into the surface zone. This replenishing of nutrients in the surface layers may be compared with a farmer's plowing the land. Each prepares the medium — soil in one case, water in the other — for the growth of a new crop.

Also the less saline surface layers tend to be relatively stable, as they are often appreciably less dense than the water beneath the halocline. Consequently, these low-salinity waters tend to remain at the surface. Such stable conditions tend to be established earlier in the spring and to persist longer near the coast than in the open ocean.

This stability of the surface water is important to phytoplankton, which must remain near the surface to obtain sunlight (see Chapter 5). If surface waters are unstable, the phytoplankton is easily mixed to depths below the surface where there is insufficient sunlight for photosynthesis. To continue our analogy with farming, the stability of the low-salinity water at the surface inhibits premature plowing before the crop has grown enough to be harvested.

Another consequence of the lower salinity of coastal surface water is that sea ice is more likely to form near the coast than in the open ocean in high latitudes. The less saline water tends to remain near the surface where it is easily cooled during local autumn and winter. Also because of its lower salinity, the water begins to freeze at higher temperatures than more saline waters. This is especially important in the Arctic Sea, as previously mentioned.

COASTAL CURRENTS

A copious discharge of fresh water may cause coastal currents. Since the existence of some coastal currents depends on an abundance of fresh water, they frequently occur only during seasons with high runoff and disappear during dry seasons.

We can explain such currents by remembering that variations in salinity cause relatively large density variations. The sea surface above low density water tends to be higher than the sea surface over more dense

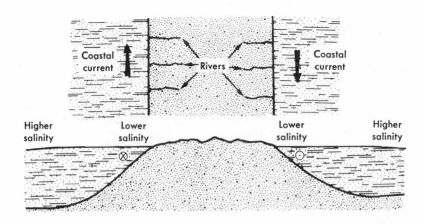

Fig. 9-1. **Sloping sea surface and coastal currents resulting from rivers discharging into coastal waters in the Northern Hemisphere.** $\otimes$ **current flowing away from you;** $\odot$ **current flowing toward you.**

water (Fig. 9-1). The resulting sloping sea surface causes a geostrophic current (see Chapter 7) flowing parallel to the coast.

The **Davidson Current** off the Washington coast is a good example of a coastal current. During the winter, numerous coastal streams discharge into the ocean. Combined with abundant rainfall along the coast, the runoff mixes with the sea water forming a nearshore band of low-salinity water, which is held near the coast by winds from the southwest.

The sea surface slopes downward from the crest of the low-salinity water hill toward the sea. The balance between the gravitational force, directed downhill, and the Coriolis effect, deflecting the current to the right, results in a northward-flowing coastal current. Offshore, the California Current continues to flow southward throughout the year (Fig. 7-1).

During the summer and autumn, rainfall and the discharge of the coastal rivers is reduced, and the winds come from the north. Without the lower salinity water along the coast, the Davidson Current gradually disappears.

ESTUARIES AND ESTUARINE CIRCULATION

Semi-enclosed tidal basins containing water with measurable amounts of sea salt are called **estuaries.** An important feature in coastal areas where runoff and precipitation exceed evaporation, estuaries serve as mixing basins for the river water and as traps for river-borne sediment. The distinguishing feature of **estuarine circulation** is the shoreward movement of subsurface sea water which first mixes with, and eventually is carried seaward by, the surface layer of less saline water (Fig. 9-2).

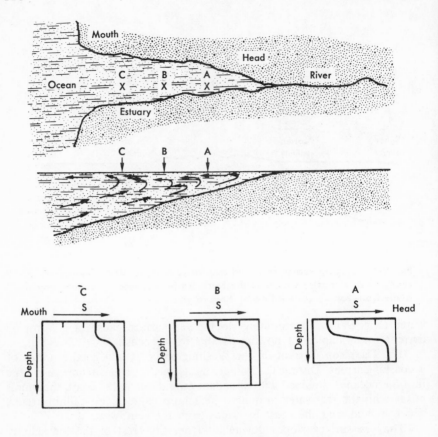

Fig. 9-2. Vertical water circulation in a simple estuary of the salt-wedge type. The variation of salinity with depth at the three stations is shown in the lower part of the figure.

Maps of coastal regions, such as the Atlantic Coast of the United States, show that estuaries come in many shapes and sizes. Such variation in geometry, combined with variations in river flow and tidal regime, results in different circulation patterns in various estuaries. We will consider only two.

The **salt-wedge estuary** (Fig. 9-2) is perhaps the most easily understood. It corresponds closely to our idealized picture of estuarine circulation where *the dense sea water flows in along the bottom to replace the salt water carried away in the surface layer.* In a relatively deep estuary with a large river flowing into it, the fresh water will tend to form a shallow layer of seaward moving water above the saline sea water. As the surface water flows seaward, it mixes with and carries seaward some of the underlying salt water.

Let us compare the amount of sea water flowing in along the estuary bottom to the amount of fresh water contributed by the river. Mixing equal volumes of river ($S=0\permil$) and sea water ($S=35\permil$) results in a salinity of approximately 17.5‰ for the mixture. Two volumes of sea water and one volume of river water results in a mixture with a salinity of approximately 23.3‰. By the time the surface water achieves a salinity of 30‰, each volume of river water has mixed with six volumes of sea water. It is obvious that the inflow of salt water along the estuary floor may be many times greater than the river discharge at the head of the estuary.

Another type of estuarine circulation is found in the **vertically homogeneous estuary** (Fig. 9-3). Instead of the well-developed halocline, such an estuary has essentially constant salinity from the top to the bottom of the water column. The water is nearly fresh at the head of the estuary, becoming more saline toward the mouth. The basic estuarine circulation operates in such an estuary, but is obscured by the extensive mixing. Usually, large tides and low river discharge in a shallow estuary cause the vertically homogeneous water column in the estuary.

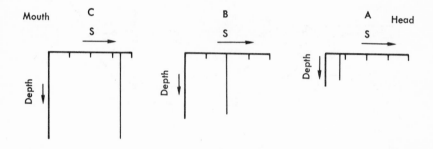

Fig. 9-3. Variation of salinity with depth at three stations in a vertically homogeneous estuary. (See Fig. 9-2 for diagram showing the station locations.)

Estuarine-like circulation is not restricted solely to estuaries. The upward movement of more saline water into a less saline surface zone is rather common in large parts of the ocean, where the surface is appreciably diluted by runoff from the land. Large areas in the Northern Indian Ocean, the North Pacific Ocean, and the Arctic Sea exhibit the basic estuarine circulation pattern.

SILLED BASINS

In estuaries or inland seas, the adjacent land masses restrict the horizontal water movements. Many such water bodies are further isolated from the adjacent ocean by a **sill,** an elevated part of the sea floor partially separating ocean basins. The sill restricts movement of the bottom waters, resulting in their partial isolation. In some instances, this isolation of bottom water is nearly total.

In a basin where the surface waters are appreciably less saline than the deeper water, an estuarine-like circulation may result. Such a circula-

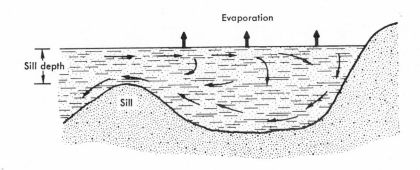

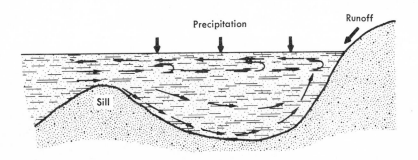

Fig. 9-4. **Water circulation in silled basins where runoff and precipitation exceed evaporation (bottom diagram) and where evaporation exceeds precipitation and runoff (top diagram).**

tion will almost entirely be restricted to the water above the sill depth (Fig. 9-4). The circulation is controlled by the amount of fresh water coming into the basin, by local winds, and by the tides.

The circulation of the water at depths below the sill top is more difficult to predict. This deeper circulation will certainly be much more sluggish than in the surface zone. Because of the halocline, the bottom water may be little affected by the surface circulation. Water density near sill depth at the basin entrance is the most important factor affecting the deeper circulation. If the water at sill depth outside the basin is appreciably denser than the water in the basin, the denser water flows into the basin and replaces the waters that previously occupied the bottom of the basin. If the water at sill depth outside the basin is less dense than that inside, the bottom waters are not replaced.

Replacing the bottom waters of a basin is essential for the maintenance of life on the basin floor and in the deeper waters. If the bottom waters are not replaced, the dissolved oxygen is eventually used up by the respiration of animals and by the decay of organic matter produced in the surface layers (see Chapter 5). When all the oxygen is gone, only certain specialized bacteria can survive.

In sea water such bacteria can obtain the oxygen necessary for their metabolic processes from the abundant sulfate ion ($SO_4^=$) in sea water. Hydrogen sulfide (H_2S), produced by these bacteria, is toxic to other organisms. As a consequence of the lack of dissolved oxygen and the presence of H_2S, the bottom waters in a stagnant basin are nearly devoid of life, except for the bacteria.

Water outside such basins usually contains appreciable amounts of dissolved oxygen. If the basin's deeper waters are replaced frequently, the dissolved oxygen will not be completely used up. Obviously, the critical factors are the rate at which the bottom waters are replaced, their initial dissolved oxygen content, and the rate of oxygen utilization in the basin.

The Black Sea is the best known example of a stagnant marine basin. Because of the highly restricted communication through the Bosporus with the Mediterranean Sea, the bottom waters of the Black Sea are almost completely isolated. It is estimated that the flow through the Bosporus would require 2,500 years to replace the waters below 30 m depth. Hydrogen sulfide occurs at all depths below 200 m, and life in the Black Sea is restricted to the surface layers.

Some Norwegian and Canadian fiords also have stagnant or nearly stagnant bottom waters containing appreciable amounts of H_2S. In other silled marine basins the bottom waters are replaced at frequent intervals and no stagnation occurs. For example, in Puget Sound — a silled, fiord-like system — the bottom waters are generally well oxygenated. Only in the most isolated parts of Puget Sound is the dissolved oxygen in the bottom waters appreciably depleted.

Not all coastal basins have an excess of fresh water in the surface layers. The Mediterranean and Red Seas and the Persian Gulf have more water removed by evaporation from the sea surface than is added through river discharge or precipitation. As a result, the surface waters become progressively more saline as they flow toward the head of such a basin (Fig. 9-4). Salinity of the surface water exceeds 40‰ at the head of the Red Sea and Persian Gulf, and it exceeds 39‰ at the eastern end of the Mediterranean Sea.

Under conditions of excess evaporation, the resulting vertical water circulation is almost the opposite of the estuarine circulation caused by excess fresh water. The surface waters become denser than those below, and they sink causing a vertical convective circulation. At the mouth there is a net inflow of surface water to replace the water lost by evaporation. There may also be a subsurface outflow of dense, warm salty water.

RIP CURRENTS AND STORM SURGES

When dealing with the open ocean, far from its boundaries, we were able to neglect certain phenomena because their effects were small. In the coastal ocean, many of these phenomena must be considered because their effects become quite noticeable. We will consider two — rip currents and storm surges.

When dealing with wind waves, we considered the fact that there are relatively small net water movements associated with waves. As you recall, we ignored this when dealing with the open ocean. At the coast, however, these wave-associated water movements toward the beach cause jet-like return flows of water away from the beach, known as **rip currents** (Fig. 9-5). These consist of three parts. The shoreward, wave-induced water movements feed water toward the beach. In the surf zone, the water flows nearly parallel to the beach. Finally, these longshore currents combine to form a jet-like stream, a few tens of meters across, which flows through the surf returning the water seaward. Rip currents extend a kilometer or two from the beach before the flow becomes too diffuse to be recognized.

On a beach, rip currents can frequently be spotted by the absence of surf in the area of the current. Usually rip currents occupy channels that are deeper than the adjacent ocean floor. Because of the greater depth in these channels, the water is usually darker in appearance.

Anyone caught in a rip current should not try to swim against the strong flow of water. By swimming parallel to the beach, one can fairly quickly get out of the seaward-flowing rip current and into quieter water.

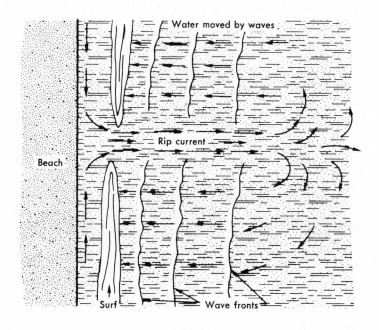

Fig. 9-5. **Water carried landward by waves flows seaward in the rip current.**

Storm surges are changes in sea level associated with a single storm. Individual storms cause small changes in sea level (usually less than a meter) around islands in the open ocean. The absence of boundaries in the open ocean permits nearly unrestricted water flow, and the storm surge is thus generally small.

Along the coast, storm surges are many times larger, occasionally causing catastrophic flooding of low-lying areas. Storm surges caused the death of 250,000 people in 1864 and 1876 around the Bay of Bengal in the Northern Indian Ocean. A storm surge in 1900 associated with a hurricane flooded Galveston, Texas, killing 6,000 people. In 1953 a severe storm in the North Sea caused sea level to rise about four meters. Storm waves overtopped and breached the dikes in the Netherlands. About 25,000 km² were flooded, 2,000 people were killed, and 600,000 people had to be evacuated.

The largest storm surges result from strong winds blowing across shallow water. Water is moved by the wind toward the upwind side of the basin, tilting the water surface. When this occurs in a shallow lake, parts of the lake floor may be uncovered.

In general, the Coriolis effect is not important in storm surges. The water moves only a short distance, and the storm lasts a relatively short time.

Prediction of dangerous storm surges is but one of the areas in which a better understanding of the oceans may pay considerable dividends for coastal inhabitants. Again we find that the oceans and atmosphere are inescapably linked. Accurate predictions of sea level are obviously impossible without the detection of storms and accurate prediction of the associated winds.

QUESTIONS

1. What is a rip current? Where and how do rip currents form?
2. What causes storm surges? List some of the factors that must be known to permit predictions.
3. Define estuary. What is the simplest estuarine flow? Describe two different types of estuarine circulation patterns. What causes them to be different?
4. What would you look for to locate a rip current at an ocean beach? If caught in one, what should you do?
5. List some important uses of the coastal oceans. Which uses tend to conflict? Which uses are compatible?
6. Why is the Coriolis effect not important in the water flow in rip currents?
7. Draw a schematic profile of the sea surface perpendicular to a Southern Hemisphere coast with a large fresh-water discharge. Indicate direction of flow in the coastal current.
8. List some of the processes causing mixing of water in the ocean. In what part of the ocean is each most important?

SUPPLEMENTARY READING

Bascom, W., "Beaches," *Scientific American,* August, 1960.
Bauer, H. B., "The Margins of the Restless Ocean," *Natural History,* vol. 68, 1959.
Bloomfield, John, *Know-How in the Surf.* Melbourne: Angus and Robertson, 1959.
Ippen, A. T., *Estuary and Coastline Hydrodynamics.* New York: McGraw-Hill Book Company, 1966. Advanced technical, mathematical treatment.
Lauff, G. H., ed., *Estuaries.* Washington, D.C.: American Association for the Advancement of Science, 1967. Technical. Collection of papers covering many aspects of estuaries.

Exponential Notation, the Metric System, and Conversion Factors

EXPONENTIAL NOTATION

In discussing the earth or its oceans, we must frequently use very large numbers. To simplify writing, reading and understanding such numbers, we employ exponential notation which indicates how many zeroes are in our number. Commonly used large numbers may be written as follows:

$10^2 = 100$ one hundred
$10^3 = 1,000$ one thousand
$10^6 = 1,000,000$ one million
$10^9 = 1,000,000,000$ one billion
$10^{12} = 1,000,000,000,000$ one million million

LENGTH

1 **kilometer (km)** $= 10^3$ meters $= 0.621$ statute miles $= 0.540$ nautical miles

1 **meter (m)** $= 10^2$ centimeters $= 39.4$ inches $= 3.28$ feet $= 1.09$ yards $= 0.547$ fathoms

1 **centimeter (cm)** $= 10$ **millimeters (mm)** $= 0.394$ inches $= 10^4$ microns (μ)

1 **micron** $(\mu) = 10^{-3}$ millimeters $= 0.000394$ inches

AREA

1 square centimeter $(\mathbf{cm}^2) = 0.155$ square inches

1 square meter $(\mathbf{m}^2) = 10.7$ square feet

1 square kilometer $(\mathbf{km}^2) = 0.386$ square statute miles $= 0.292$ square nautical miles.

VOLUME

1 **cubic kilometer** $(\mathbf{km}^3) = 10^9$ cubic meters $= 10^{15}$ cubic centimeters $= 0.24$ cubic statute miles

1 **cubic meter** (m³) = 10⁶ cubic centimeters = 10³ liters = 35.3 cubic feet = 264 U.S. gallons

1 **liter** = 10³ cubic centimeters = 1.06 quarts = 0.264 U.S. gallons

1 **cubic centimeter** (cm³) = 0.061 cubic inches

MASS

1 **metric ton** = 10⁶ grams = 2,205 pounds

1 **kilogram** (kg) = 10³ grams = 2.205 pounds

1 **gram** (g) = 0.035 ounce

SPEED

1 **knot** (nautical mile per hour) = 1.15 statute miles per hour = 0.51 meter per second

1 **meter per second** (m/sec) = 2.24 statute miles per hour = 1.94 knots

1 **centimeter per second** (cm/sec) = 1.97 feet per second

TEMPERATURE

	Celsius (°C) (also °Centigrade)	Fahrenheit (°F)
Boiling point of water	100	212
Melting point of ice	0	32
Conversion formulas		

$$°C = \frac{°F - 32}{1.8}$$

$$°F = 1.8(°C) + 32$$

ENERGY

1 gram-calorie (usually **calorie, cal**) = 1/860 watt-hour = 1/252 British Thermal Units (B.T.U.)

Index

Index